MW00651522

national electrical code®

illustrated changes based on the 1996 NEC®

AMERICAN TECHNICAL PUBLISHERS, INC.
HOMEWOOD, ILLINOIS 60430

R. T. Miller

1 2 3 4 5 6 7 8 9 – 95 – 9 8 7 6 5 4 3 2 1

Printed in the United States of America

ISBN 0-8269-1530-2

CONTENTS

INTRODUCTION

National Electrical Code® Illustrated Changes Based on the 1996 NEC® is designed to show, and briefly describe, many of the changes made to update the 1993 NEC®. This book may be used for classroom instruction, individual study, and in electrical seminars.

Information in the lower left-hand corner of each NEC® change gives the Article subject, Article number, and type of change. The text briefly discusses the change and the illustration shows the change. The large, bold-face type on each illustrated change gives the subject and NEC® reference for each illustrated change. *Illustrated Changes* shows and/or describes over 350 changes that were made for the 1996 NEC®.

National Electrical Code® Changes Workbook Based on the 1996 NEC® may be used in conjunction with this book for a comprehensive course detailing changes in the 1996 NEC®. See Appendix. *Changes Workbook* contains 29 tests plus the Final Exam covering changes in the 1996 NEC®.

The Appendix contains a listing of abbreviations and symbols used in *National Electrical Code® Illustrated Changes Based on the 1996 NEC®*. Also included is Related Material from American Technical Publishers, Inc.

The Publisher

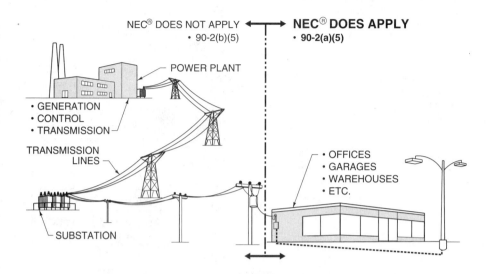

INTRODUCTION

90-2(a)(5)

REVISION

The text of Subsection (5) has been revised to clarify that only those installations that are an integral part of the electrical utilities generation, transmission, or control of power are excluded from the scope of the NEC®.

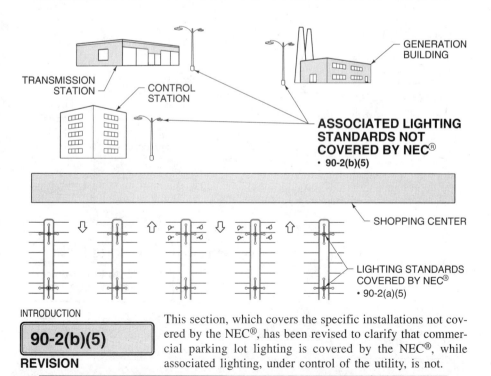

INTRODUCTION

90-2(b)(5)

REVISION

This section, which covers the specific installations not covered by the NEC®, has been revised to clarify that commercial parking lot lighting is covered by the NEC®, while associated lighting, under control of the utility, is not.

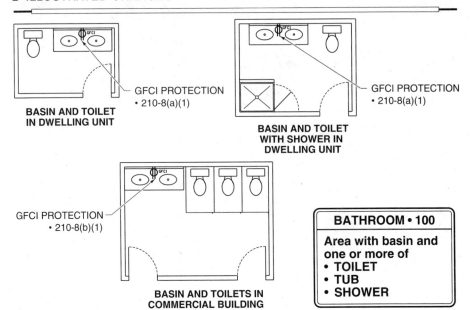

GFCI PROTECTION
• 210-8(a)(1)

**BASIN AND TOILET
IN DWELLING UNIT**

GFCI PROTECTION
• 210-8(a)(1)

**BASIN AND TOILET
WITH SHOWER IN
DWELLING UNIT**

GFCI PROTECTION
• 210-8(b)(1)

**BASIN AND TOILETS IN
COMMERCIAL BUILDING**

BATHROOM • 100

**Area with basin and
one or more of
• TOILET
• TUB
• SHOWER**

DEFINITIONS

100

NEW DEFINITION

The definition of *bathroom*, which appears in more than two articles, has been relocated to 100. Article 100, Definitions, applies throughout the entire NEC®.

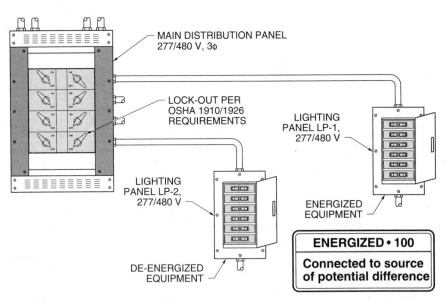

MAIN DISTRIBUTION PANEL
277/480 V, 3φ

LOCK-OUT PER
OSHA 1910/1926
REQUIREMENTS

LIGHTING
PANEL LP-1,
277/480 V

LIGHTING
PANEL LP-2,
277/480 V

ENERGIZED
EQUIPMENT

DE-ENERGIZED
EQUIPMENT

ENERGIZED • 100

**Connected to source
of potential difference**

DEFINITIONS

100

NEW DEFINITION

A definition of *energize*d has been added to 100 because the term is used in many articles in the NEC® without being defined. The definition is taken from the NFPA, NEC® Manual of Style.

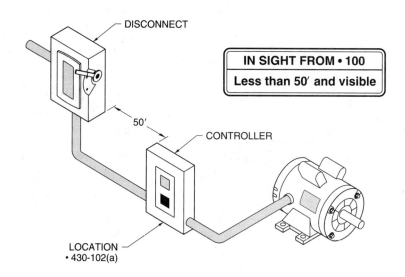

IN SIGHT FROM • 100

Less than 50′ and visible

DISCONNECT

50′

CONTROLLER

LOCATION
• 430-102(a)

DEFINITIONS

100

REVISION

The definition of *in sight from* has been revised to clarify that when equipment is required by the NEC® to be in sight from other equipment, it shall be within 50′ and visible.

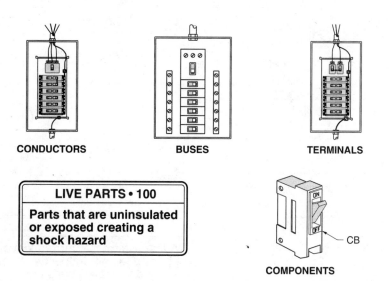

CONDUCTORS   **BUSES**   **TERMINALS**

LIVE PARTS • 100

Parts that are uninsulated or exposed creating a shock hazard

CB

COMPONENTS

DEFINITIONS

100

NEW DEFINITION

A definition of *live parts* has been added to 100 because the term is used in many articles in the NEC® without being defined. The definition is taken from NFPA, NEC® Manual of Style.

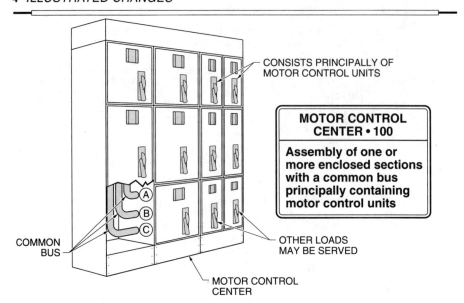

CONSISTS PRINCIPALLY OF
MOTOR CONTROL UNITS

**MOTOR CONTROL
CENTER • 100**

**Assembly of one or
more enclosed sections
with a common bus
principally containing
motor control units**

COMMON
BUS

Ⓐ
Ⓑ
Ⓒ

OTHER LOADS
MAY BE SERVED

MOTOR CONTROL
CENTER

DEFINITIONS

100

NEW DEFINITION

CMP-1 has added a new definition to 100 for *motor control center.* The new definition is identical to one that appears in 430-92. The motor control center is required to consist principally of motor control units, although other loads may be served by the center.

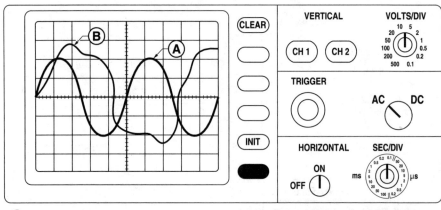

Ⓐ APPLIED VOLTAGE

Ⓑ DISTORTED WAVE FORM

NONLINEAR LOAD • 100

**A load where the current wave
shape does not follow the
applied voltage wave shape**

DEFINITIONS

100

NEW DEFINITION

A definition of *nonlinear load* now appears in 100. In addition, a FPN has been added below the definition to specify some of the types of equipment that can cause nonlinear loads.

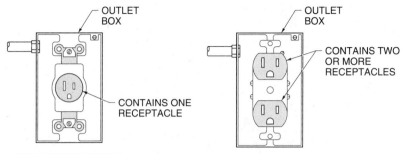

OUTLET BOX

CONTAINS ONE RECEPTACLE

SINGLE RECEPTACLE

OUTLET BOX

CONTAINS TWO OR MORE RECEPTACLES

MULTIPLE RECEPTACLE

RECEPTACLE • 100
A contact device installed at an outlet for connecting a single contact device

DEFINITIONS

100

REVISION

The definition of *receptacle* has been revised to incorporate the FPN into the main rule. The FPN contained language which could be considered mandatory, which is a violation of the NEC® Manual of Style and 90-5.

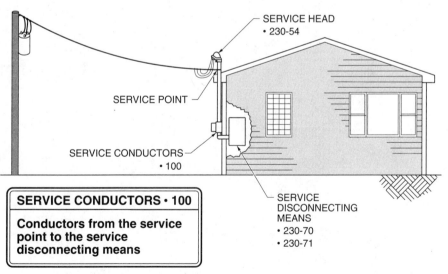

SERVICE HEAD • 230-54

SERVICE POINT

SERVICE CONDUCTORS • 100

SERVICE DISCONNECTING MEANS • 230-70 • 230-71

SERVICE CONDUCTORS • 100
Conductors from the service point to the service disconnecting means

DEFINITIONS

100

NEW DEFINITION

The definition of *service conductors,* which appeared in 230-10, has been revised and relocated to 100. The new definition clarifies, without mandatory language, that the conductors from the service point to the service disconnecting means are service conductors.

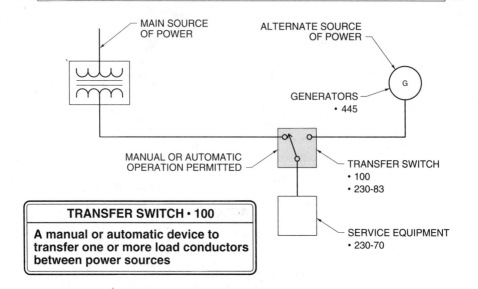

MAIN SOURCE OF POWER

ALTERNATE SOURCE OF POWER

GENERATORS
• 445

MANUAL OR AUTOMATIC OPERATION PERMITTED

TRANSFER SWITCH
• 100
• 230-83

TRANSFER SWITCH • 100

A manual or automatic device to transfer one or more load conductors between power sources

SERVICE EQUIPMENT
• 230-70

DEFINITIONS

100

REVISION

The definition of *transfer switch* has been revised to incorporate the FPN into the actual definition. By definition, transfer switches can operate either manually or automatically.

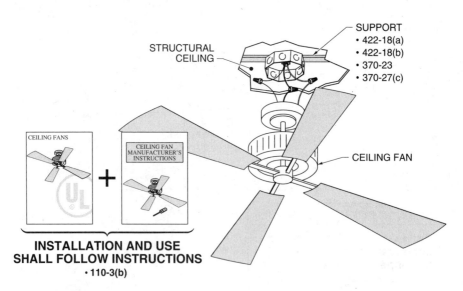

SUPPORT
• 422-18(a)
• 422-18(b)
• 370-23
• 370-27(c)

STRUCTURAL CEILING

CEILING FANS

CEILING FAN MANUFACTURER'S INSTRUCTIONS

+

CEILING FAN

INSTALLATION AND USE SHALL FOLLOW INSTRUCTIONS
• 110-3(b)

REQUIREMENTS FOR ELECTRICAL INSTALLATIONS

110-3(b)

REVISION

The revision clarifies the requirements of this section for following manufacturers' instructions. Some equipment, such as ceiling fans, may include specific instructions for their installation and use. This change requires that the installation and use follow instructions.

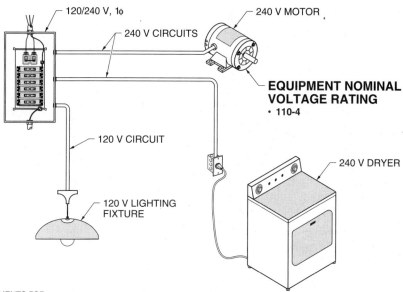

REQUIREMENTS FOR
ELECTRICAL INSTALLATIONS

110-4

REVISION

A new second sentence has been added to this section which requires that all equipment have a nominal voltage rating which is not less than the circuit nominal voltage rating to which it is connected.

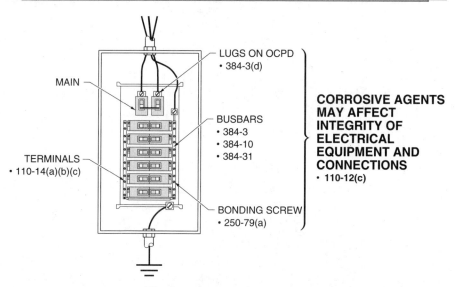

REQUIREMENTS FOR
ELECTRICAL INSTALLATIONS

110-12(c)

REVISION

The first sentence of this section has been revised to include corrosive agents among the foreign materials that may affect the integrity of the internal parts of electrical equipment. A new second sentence has been added which requires that equipment cannot be subject to conditions or elements that may affect its safe operation or mechanical strength.

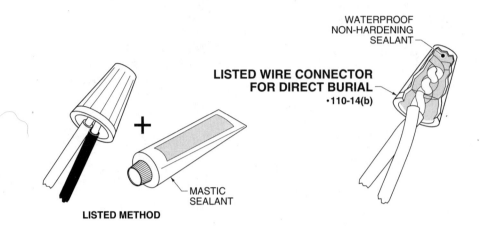

WATERPROOF
NON-HARDENING
SEALANT

**LISTED WIRE CONNECTOR
FOR DIRECT BURIAL**
•110-14(b)

MASTIC
SEALANT

LISTED METHOD

REQUIREMENTS FOR
ELECTRICAL INSTALLATIONS

110-14(b)

REVISION

A new paragraph has been added to this section which requires that devices intended for connecting or splicing conductors underground be listed for direct burial use. Wire connectors are available which contain water repellent sealant which ensures that the conductor connection can withstand the elements.

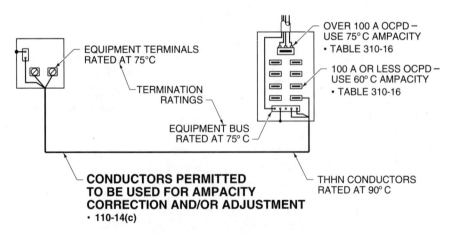

OVER 100 A OCPD –
USE 75°C AMPACITY
• TABLE 310-16

EQUIPMENT TERMINALS
RATED AT 75°C

100 A OR LESS OCPD –
USE 60° C AMPACITY
• TABLE 310-16

TERMINATION
RATINGS

EQUIPMENT BUS
RATED AT 75° C

**CONDUCTORS PERMITTED
TO BE USED FOR AMPACITY
CORRECTION AND/OR ADJUSTMENT**
• 110-14(c)

THHN CONDUCTORS
RATED AT 90° C

REQUIREMENTS FOR
ELECTRICAL INSTALLATIONS

110-14(c)

REVISION

This section covering temperature limitations has been revised with the addition of a new sentence which clarifies that conductors with temperature ratings higher than the terminations are permitted to be used provided the conductor ampacity is based on the lower of the two ratings. This essentially allows the conductors' higher temperature rating to be used for derating purposes.

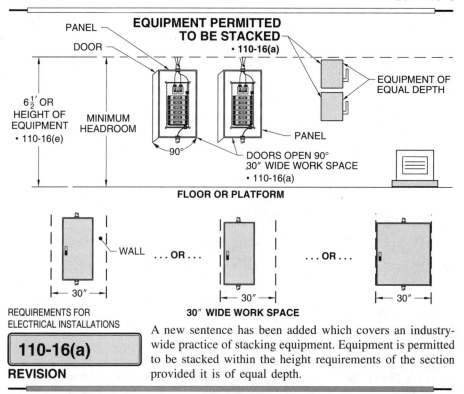

EQUIPMENT PERMITTED TO BE STACKED
• 110-16(a)

PANEL
DOOR
EQUIPMENT OF EQUAL DEPTH
6½' OR HEIGHT OF EQUIPMENT • 110-16(e)
MINIMUM HEADROOM
PANEL
90°
DOORS OPEN 90° 30" WIDE WORK SPACE • 110-16(a)
FLOOR OR PLATFORM

WALL ...OR... ...OR...
30" 30" 30"
30" WIDE WORK SPACE

REQUIREMENTS FOR ELECTRICAL INSTALLATIONS

110-16(a)

REVISION

A new sentence has been added which covers an industry-wide practice of stacking equipment. Equipment is permitted to be stacked within the height requirements of the section provided it is of equal depth.

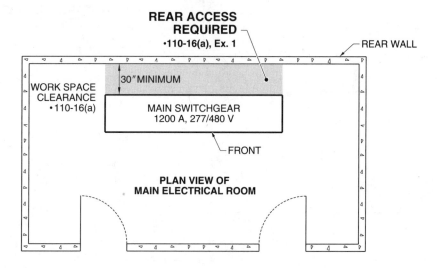

REAR ACCESS REQUIRED
•110-16(a), Ex. 1
REAR WALL

WORK SPACE CLEARANCE •110-16(a)
30" MINIMUM
MAIN SWITCHGEAR 1200 A, 277/480 V
FRONT

PLAN VIEW OF MAIN ELECTRICAL ROOM

REQUIREMENTS FOR ELECTRICAL INSTALLATIONS

110-16(a), Ex. 1

REVISION

Ex. 1 has been modified to require that electrical equipment, for which rear access is required to work on de-energized components, be provided with a minimum of 30" horizontal work space clearance.

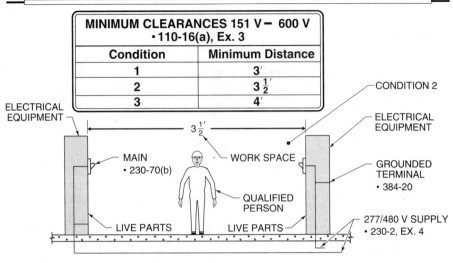

MINIMUM CLEARANCES 151 V — 600 V • 110-16(a), Ex. 3	
Condition	Minimum Distance
1	3'
2	$3\frac{1}{2}'$
3	4'

This exception reduces minimum work space clearance from 4' to $3\frac{1}{2}'$ for retrofit installations in existing buildings.

REQUIREMENTS FOR
ELECTRICAL INSTALLATIONS

110-16(a), Ex. 3

NEW EXCEPTION

The exception applies to electrical equipment installed on both sides of an aisle. The reduction in work space is permitted only if written procedures are in place ensuring that equipment on one side of the aisle is worked on at a time and the service work is performed by qualified persons.

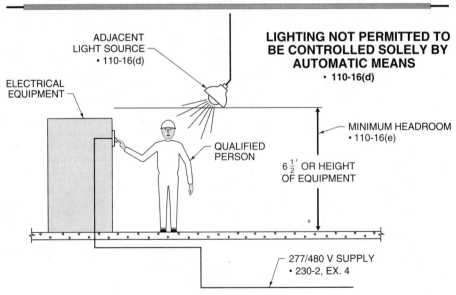

LIGHTING NOT PERMITTED TO
BE CONTROLLED SOLELY BY
AUTOMATIC MEANS
• 110-16(d)

Two revisions to this section have been made. The first change incorporates the FPN into the general rule. This specifies that adjacent light sources can provide the illumination required by this section. The second change prohibits the use of automatic means only, such as motion detectors, to control the lighting in electrical equipment rooms.

REQUIREMENTS FOR
ELECTRICAL INSTALLATIONS

110-16(d)

REVISION

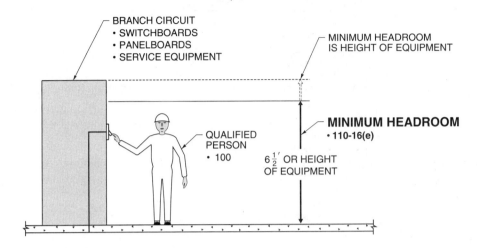

BRANCH CIRCUIT
• SWITCHBOARDS
• PANELBOARDS
• SERVICE EQUIPMENT

MINIMUM HEADROOM
IS HEIGHT OF EQUIPMENT

MINIMUM HEADROOM
• 110-16(e)

QUALIFIED
PERSON
• 100

$6\frac{1}{2}'$ OR HEIGHT
OF EQUIPMENT

REQUIREMENTS FOR
ELECTRICAL INSTALLATIONS

110-16(e)
REVISION

The requirements for minimum headroom clearances have been modified to specify that the minimum height required is $6\frac{1}{2}'$ about electrical equipment. Where the equipment itself exceeds the $6\frac{1}{2}'$, the headroom clearance shall extend to the height of the equipment.

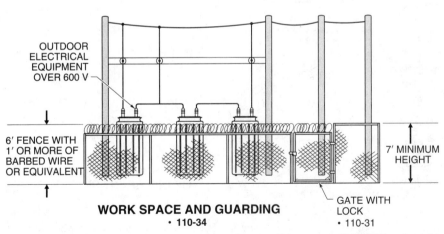

OUTDOOR
ELECTRICAL
EQUIPMENT
OVER 600 V

6' FENCE WITH
1' OR MORE OF
BARBED WIRE
OR EQUIVALENT

7' MINIMUM
HEIGHT

WORK SPACE AND GUARDING
• 110-34

GATE WITH
LOCK
• 110-31

REQUIREMENTS FOR
ELECTRICAL INSTALLATIONS

110-31
REVISION

The requirements for a wall, screen, or fence around outdoor electrical equipment exceeding 600 V, nominal, have been modified by including the text of FPN 3 in the general rule. This requirement states that a fence shall be at least 7' in height. A fence is permitted to be 6' in height if it is provided with an extension of at least 1' of barbed wire or equivalent.

DETERMINING CONDUCTOR AMPACITY

What is the ampacity of three direct burial #3/0 AL conductors with a temperature rating of 90°C used for a 4160 V feeder?

Table 310-82: #3/0 = 300 A
Note 5 of Notes to Tables 310-69− 310-86; 110-40: 90°C rating per Detail 9
Ampacity = **300 A**

**TEMPERATURE
LIMITATION
REQUIREMENTS**
• 110-40

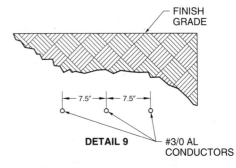

FINISH GRADE

7.5″ 7.5″

DETAIL 9 #3/0 AL CONDUCTORS

REQUIREMENTS FOR
ELECTRICAL INSTALLATIONS

110-40

NEW SECTION

This change provides for temperature limitation requirements for medium voltage conductors and their terminations, much like that already required for conductors of 600 V or less in 110-14(c).

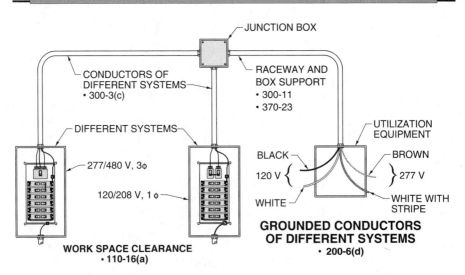

JUNCTION BOX

CONDUCTORS OF
DIFFERENT SYSTEMS
• 300-3(c)

RACEWAY AND
BOX SUPPORT
• 300-11
• 370-23

DIFFERENT SYSTEMS

UTILIZATION
EQUIPMENT

277/480 V, 3φ

120/208 V, 1 φ

BLACK
120 V {
WHITE

BROWN
} 277 V
WHITE WITH
STRIPE

WORK SPACE CLEARANCE
• 110-16(a)

**GROUNDED CONDUCTORS
OF DIFFERENT SYSTEMS**
• 200-6(d)

USE AND INDENTIFICATION
OF GROUNDED CONDUCTORS

200-6(d)

REVISION

This section has been revised to clarify that when grounded conductors from different electrical systems are installed in the same raceway, cable, enclosure, etc., one grounded conductor shall be white or gray and the other shall be white with a readily distinguishable, different colored stripe. The stripe shall run along the outer covering or insulation of the conductor and it shall not be the color green.

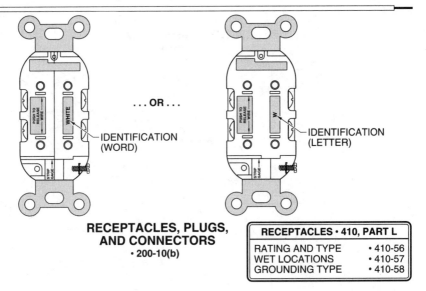

... OR ...

IDENTIFICATION (WORD)

IDENTIFICATION (LETTER)

RECEPTACLES, PLUGS, AND CONNECTORS
· 200-10(b)

RECEPTACLES · 410, PART L	
RATING AND TYPE	· 410-56
WET LOCATIONS	· 410-57
GROUNDING TYPE	· 410-58

USE AND IDENTIFICATION
OF GROUNDED CONDUCTORS

200-10(b)
REVISION

In an effort to harmonize the Canadian Electrical Code with the NEC®, CMP-5 has accepted a proposal to permit the termination point on receptacles, attachment plugs, and cord connectors for the grounded conductor to be marked with a letter "W" instead of just the word "white" or the color white as is presently required.

BRANCH CIRCUITS

210-6(c)(1)
REVISION

Electric-discharge lighting fixtures of all types, not just those with medium-base screw-shell lampholders, are permitted to be supplied by 277 V circuits provided the fixtures are listed.

BRANCH CIRCUITS

210-6(c)(2)
REVISION

Incandescent lighting fixtures of all types, not just those with medium-base screw-shell lampholders, are permitted to be supplied by 277 V circuits provided the fixtures are listed.

RECEPTACLE REPLACEMENT
• 210-7(d)

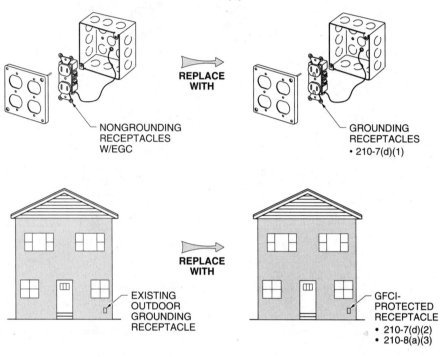

REPLACE WITH

NONGROUNDING RECEPTACLES W/EGC

GROUNDING RECEPTACLES
• 210-7(d)(1)

REPLACE WITH

EXISTING OUTDOOR GROUNDING RECEPTACLE

GFCI-PROTECTED RECEPTACLE
• 210-7(d)(2)
• 210-8(a)(3)

REPLACE WITH

NONGROUNDING RECEPTACLES W/O EGC

NONGROUNDING RECEPTACLE
• 210-7(d)(3)a

GFCI RECEPTACLE "NO EQUIPMENT GROUND"
• 210-7(d)(3)b

GROUNDING RECEPTACLE
• 210-7(d)(3)c
• 250-50(b), Ex.

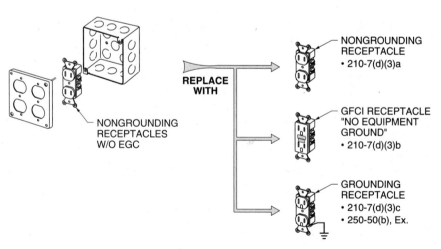

BRANCH CIRCUITS

210-7(d)
REVISION

The entire section has been rewritten to clarify the requirements for replacement of receptacles.

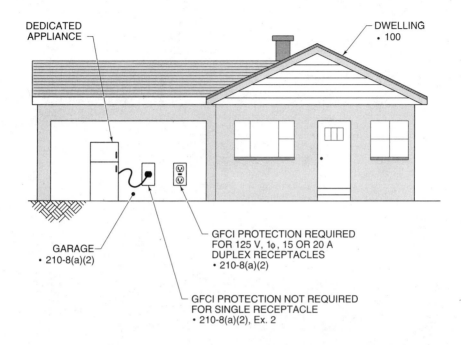

DEDICATED
APPLIANCE

DWELLING
• 100

GARAGE
• 210-8(a)(2)

GFCI PROTECTION REQUIRED
FOR 125 V, 1φ, 15 OR 20 A
DUPLEX RECEPTACLES
• 210-8(a)(2)

GFCI PROTECTION NOT REQUIRED
FOR SINGLE RECEPTACLE
• 210-8(a)(2), Ex. 2

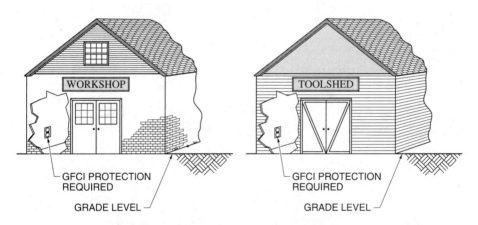

WORKSHOP

TOOLSHED

GFCI PROTECTION
REQUIRED

GFCI PROTECTION
REQUIRED

GRADE LEVEL

GRADE LEVEL

**UNFINISHED ACCESSORY BUILDINGS
NOW REQUIRE GFCI PROTECTION**
•**210-8(a)(2)**

BRANCH CIRCUITS

210-8(a)(2)

REVISION

This section covering GFCI protection for garages has been expanded to include other buildings or structures such as workshops or storage sheds with grade-level access.

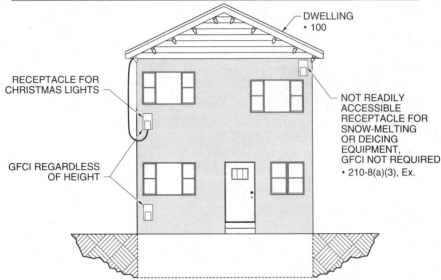

DWELLING
• 100

RECEPTACLE FOR
CHRISTMAS LIGHTS

NOT READILY
ACCESSIBLE
RECEPTACLE FOR
SNOW-MELTING
OR DEICING
EQUIPMENT,
GFCI NOT REQUIRED
• 210-8(a)(3), Ex.

GFCI REGARDLESS
OF HEIGHT

GFCI PROTECTION REQUIRED OUTDOORS ON DWELLING UNITS
• 210-8(a)(3)

BRANCH CIRCUITS

210-8(a)(3)

REVISION

GFCI protection for outdoor receptacles, installed at dwelling units, include all outdoor receptacles, except those that are not readily accessible and are supplied from a dedicated branch circuit for snow-melting equipment.

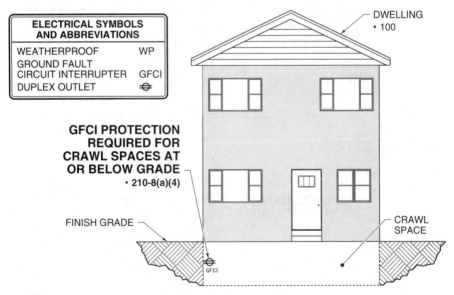

ELECTRICAL SYMBOLS AND ABBREVIATIONS	
WEATHERPROOF	WP
GROUND FAULT CIRCUIT INTERRUPTER	GFCI
DUPLEX OUTLET	⊖

DWELLING
• 100

**GFCI PROTECTION
REQUIRED FOR
CRAWL SPACES AT
OR BELOW GRADE**
• 210-8(a)(4)

FINISH GRADE

CRAWL
SPACE

GFCI

BRANCH CIRCUITS

210-8(a)(4)

REVISION

GFCI requirements for crawl spaces and unfinished basements have been revised by separating the two locations. All receptacles installed in crawl spaces of dwelling units, that are at or below grade, are required to have GFCI protection.

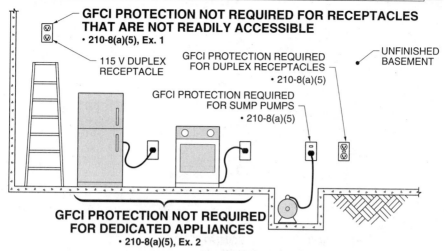

GFCI PROTECTION NOT REQUIRED FOR RECEPTACLES THAT ARE NOT READILY ACCESSIBLE
• 210-8(a)(5), Ex. 1

115 V DUPLEX RECEPTACLE

GFCI PROTECTION REQUIRED FOR DUPLEX RECEPTACLES
• 210-8(a)(5)

UNFINISHED BASEMENT

GFCI PROTECTION REQUIRED FOR SUMP PUMPS
• 210-8(a)(5)

GFCI PROTECTION NOT REQUIRED FOR DEDICATED APPLIANCES
• 210-8(a)(5), Ex. 2

BRANCH CIRCUITS

210-8(a)(5)

REVISION

The exceptions for GFCI protection in dwelling unit unfinished basements have been modified. Ex. 1 now permits receptacles that are not readily accessible to be installed without GFCI protection. Ex. 2 allows for the installation of a single or duplex receptacle, without GFCI protection, provided the appliance(s) served occupy a dedicated space and are not easily moved from place to place. The exception for sump pumps has been deleted.

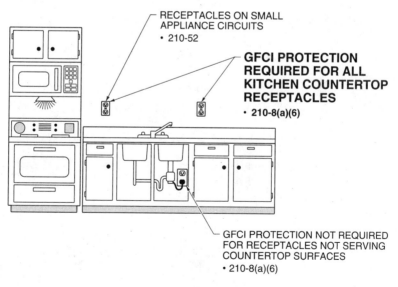

RECEPTACLES ON SMALL APPLIANCE CIRCUITS
• 210-52

GFCI PROTECTION REQUIRED FOR ALL KITCHEN COUNTERTOP RECEPTACLES
• 210-8(a)(6)

GFCI PROTECTION NOT REQUIRED FOR RECEPTACLES NOT SERVING COUNTERTOP SURFACES
• 210-8(a)(6)

BRANCH CIRCUITS

210-8(a)(6)

REVISION

The 6′ limitation for kitchen countertop receptacles has been deleted. All receptacles intended to serve countertop surfaces shall be provided with GFCI protection.

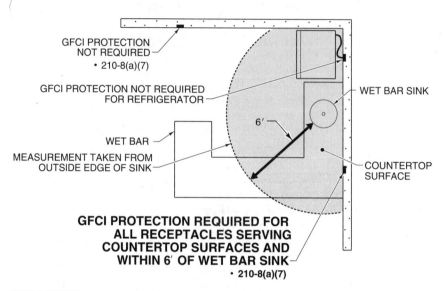

GFCI PROTECTION
NOT REQUIRED
• 210-8(a)(7)

GFCI PROTECTION NOT REQUIRED
FOR REFRIGERATOR

WET BAR SINK

6'

WET BAR

MEASUREMENT TAKEN FROM
OUTSIDE EDGE OF SINK

COUNTERTOP
SURFACE

**GFCI PROTECTION REQUIRED FOR
ALL RECEPTACLES SERVING
COUNTERTOP SURFACES AND
WITHIN 6' OF WET BAR SINK**
• **210-8(a)(7)**

BRANCH CIRCUITS

210-8(a)(7)

REVISION

The requirement for GFCI protection for receptacles installed within 6' of a wet bar sink has been revised to clarify that the 6' measurement shall be taken from the outside edge of the sink.

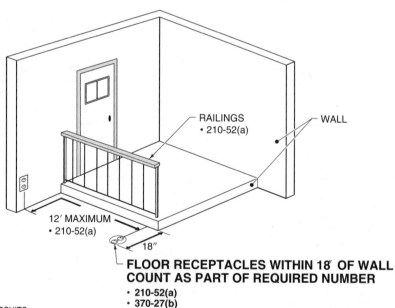

RAILINGS
• 210-52(a)

WALL

12' MAXIMUM
• 210-52(a)

18"

**FLOOR RECEPTACLES WITHIN 18" OF WALL
COUNT AS PART OF REQUIRED NUMBER**
• **210-52(a)**
• **370-27(b)**

BRANCH CIRCUITS

210-52(a)

REVISION

A receptacle outlet, located in the floor, shall be installed within 18" of the wall, to be counted as the required receptacle outlet specified in 210-52(a).

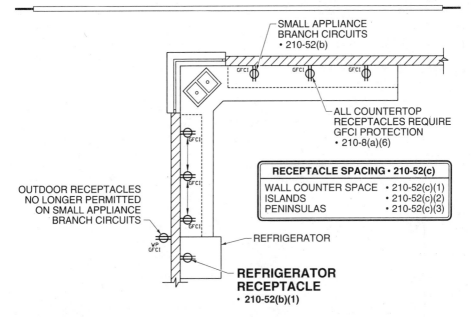

SMALL APPLIANCE
BRANCH CIRCUITS
• 210-52(b)

ALL COUNTERTOP
RECEPTACLES REQUIRE
GFCI PROTECTION
• 210-8(a)(6)

RECEPTACLE SPACING • 210-52(c)	
WALL COUNTER SPACE	• 210-52(c)(1)
ISLANDS	• 210-52(c)(2)
PENINSULAS	• 210-52(c)(3)

OUTDOOR RECEPTACLES
NO LONGER PERMITTED
ON SMALL APPLIANCE
BRANCH CIRCUITS

REFRIGERATOR

**REFRIGERATOR
RECEPTACLE**
• **210-52(b)(1)**

BRANCH CIRCUITS

210-52(b)(1)

REVISION

The requirements for small appliance branch circuits have been revised to clarify that only the receptacle outlets covered by 210-52(a) and 210-52(c), and the outlet for refrigeration equipment are required to be on the small appliance branch circuit.

RECEPTACLES ON SMALL
APPLIANCE CIRCUITS
• 210-52(b)

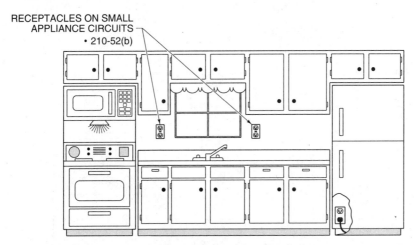

**INDIVIDUAL 15 A BRANCH
CIRCUIT PERMITTED
FOR REFRIGERATOR**
• **210-52(b)(1), Ex. 2**

BRANCH CIRCUITS

210-52(b)(1), Ex. 2

NEW EXCEPTION

A new exception has been included to permit the receptacle outlet for the refrigerator to be installed on a 15 A or greater, individual branch circuit.

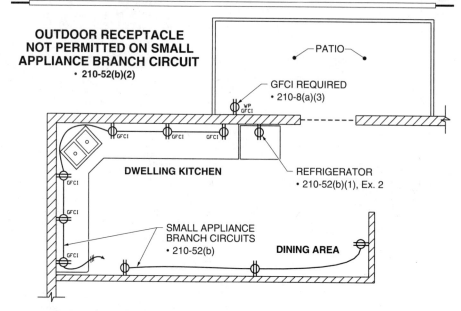

OUTDOOR RECEPTACLE NOT PERMITTED ON SMALL APPLIANCE BRANCH CIRCUIT
• 210-52(b)(2)

—PATIO—

GFCI REQUIRED
• 210-8(a)(3)

WP GFCI

GFCI GFCI GFCI

DWELLING KITCHEN

REFRIGERATOR
• 210-52(b)(1), Ex. 2

GFCI

GFCI

SMALL APPLIANCE BRANCH CIRCUITS
• 210-52(b)

DINING AREA

GFCI

BRANCH CIRCUITS

210-52(b)(2)
REVISION

The exception which permitted outdoor receptacles to be installed on the small appliance branch circuit has been removed.

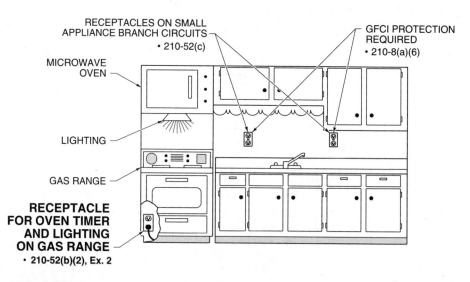

RECEPTACLES ON SMALL APPLIANCE BRANCH CIRCUITS
• 210-52(c)

GFCI PROTECTION REQUIRED
• 210-8(a)(6)

MICROWAVE OVEN

LIGHTING

GAS RANGE

RECEPTACLE FOR OVEN TIMER AND LIGHTING ON GAS RANGE
• 210-52(b)(2), Ex. 2

BRANCH CIRCUITS

210-52(b)(2), Ex. 2
REVISION

The permission to install receptacles for auxiliary equipment on gas-fired ranges on the small appliance branch circuit has been revised to include supplemental equipment and lighting.

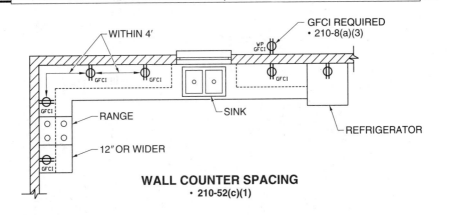

WALL COUNTER SPACING
• 210-52(c)(1)

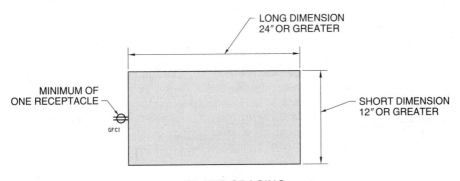

ISLAND SPACING
• 210-52(c)(2)

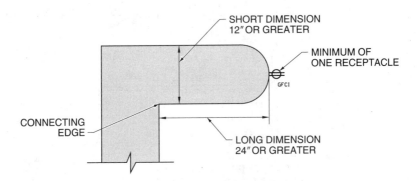

PENINSULAR SPACING
• 210-52(c)(3)

BRANCH CIRCUITS

210-52(c)

REVISION

The entire subpart has been revised and rearranged to allow for easier application and understanding of kitchen counter-top receptacle requirements.

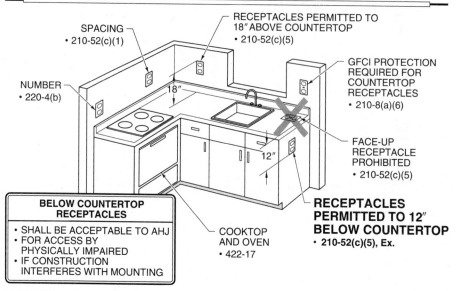

SPACING
• 210-52(c)(1)

RECEPTACLES PERMITTED TO
18″ ABOVE COUNTERTOP
• 210-52(c)(5)

GFCI PROTECTION
REQUIRED FOR
COUNTERTOP
RECEPTACLES
• 210-8(a)(6)

NUMBER
• 220-4(b)

18″

FACE-UP
RECEPTACLE
PROHIBITED
• 210-52(c)(5)

12″

**BELOW COUNTERTOP
RECEPTACLES**

• SHALL BE ACCEPTABLE TO AHJ
• FOR ACCESS BY
  PHYSICALLY IMPAIRED
• IF CONSTRUCTION
  INTERFERES WITH MOUNTING

COOKTOP
AND OVEN
• 422-17

**RECEPTACLES
PERMITTED TO 12″
BELOW COUNTERTOP**
• **210-52(c)(5), Ex.**

BRANCH CIRCUITS

210-52(c)(5), Ex.

NEW EXCEPTION

An exception has been added to permit receptacles to be installed not more than 12″ below the countertop surface provided the installation is acceptable to the AHJ and it is necessary for access by the physically impaired, or the construction of the island or peninsula interferes with the mounting.

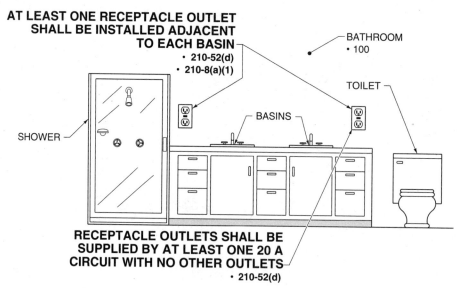

**AT LEAST ONE RECEPTACLE OUTLET
SHALL BE INSTALLED ADJACENT
TO EACH BASIN**
• **210-52(d)**
• **210-8(a)(1)**

BATHROOM
• 100

TOILET

SHOWER

BASINS

**RECEPTACLE OUTLETS SHALL BE
SUPPLIED BY AT LEAST ONE 20 A
CIRCUIT WITH NO OTHER OUTLETS**
• **210-52(d)**

BRANCH CIRCUITS

210-52(d)

REVISION

Receptacle outlets, located in dwelling unit bathrooms, shall be supplied by a dedicated 20 A branch circuit. No other outlets are permitted to be installed on the circuit.

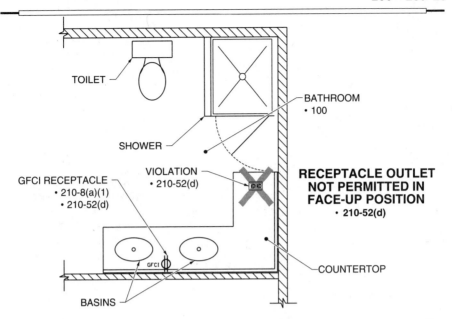

TOILET

BATHROOM
• 100

SHOWER

VIOLATION
• 210-52(d)

GFCI RECEPTACLE
• 210-8(a)(1)
• 210-52(d)

RECEPTACLE OUTLET
NOT PERMITTED IN
FACE-UP POSITION
• 210-52(d)

COUNTERTOP

BASINS

BRANCH CIRCUITS

210-52(d)
REVISION

A new sentence has been added which requires that receptacle outlets installed in bathrooms are not permitted to be installed in the face-up position if they are located in bathroom basin countertops or work surfaces.

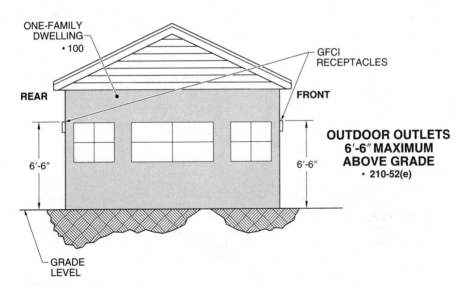

ONE-FAMILY
DWELLING
• 100

GFCI
RECEPTACLES

REAR

FRONT

OUTDOOR OUTLETS
6'-6" MAXIMUM
ABOVE GRADE
• 210-52(e)

6'-6"

6'-6"

GRADE
LEVEL

BRANCH CIRCUITS

210-52(e)
REVISION

The requirements for outdoor receptacles installed at dwelling units have been revised so that the required receptacle(s) shall be installed at a location not more than 6'-6" above grade.

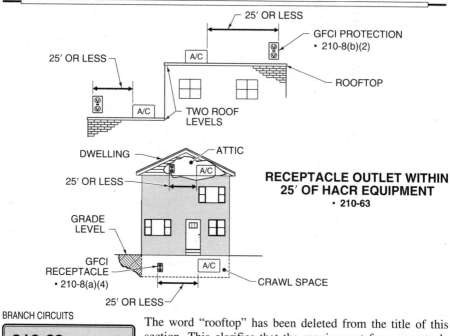

RECEPTACLE OUTLET WITHIN
25' OF HACR EQUIPMENT
• 210-63

BRANCH CIRCUITS

210-63

REVISION

The word "rooftop" has been deleted from the title of this section. This clarifies that the requirement for a receptacle outlet within 25' of HACR equipment applies whether it is installed on the roof, in an attic, or in a crawl space.

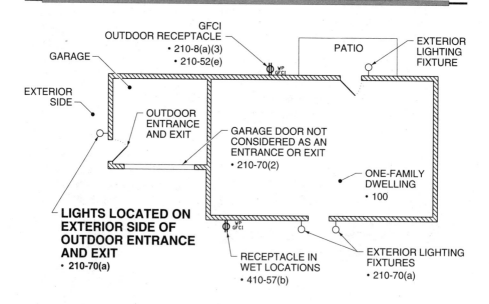

BRANCH CIRCUITS

210-70(a)

REVISION

This section has been revised by specifying that the lighting outlet required for outdoor entrances and exits shall be installed outside of the entrance or exit.

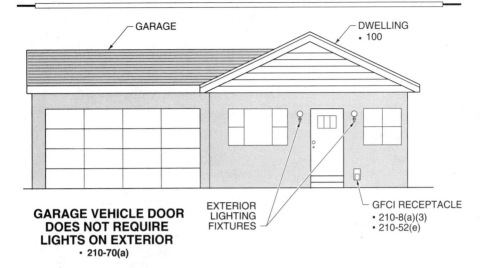

**GARAGE VEHICLE DOOR
DOES NOT REQUIRE
LIGHTS ON EXTERIOR**
• 210-70(a)

GARAGE

DWELLING
• 100

EXTERIOR
LIGHTING
FIXTURES

GFCI RECEPTACLE
• 210-8(a)(3)
• 210-52(e)

BRANCH CIRCUITS

| **210-70(a)**
REVISION |

The FPN, which clarified that a garage vehicle door should not be considered an outdoor entrance, has been incorporated into the general rule of this section.

**OCCUPANCY SENSORS CAN
SUPPLEMENT WALL SWITCHES
BUT CANNOT REPLACE THEM**
• 210-70(a), Ex. 3

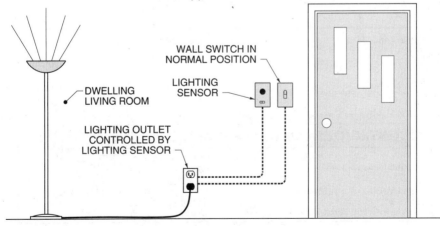

WALL SWITCH IN
NORMAL POSITION

DWELLING
LIVING ROOM

LIGHTING
SENSOR

LIGHTING OUTLET
CONTROLLED BY
LIGHTING SENSOR

BRANCH CIRCUITS

210-70(a), Ex. 3
NEW EXCEPTION

A new exception has been added which permits occupancy sensors to control lighting outlets provided the sensors are installed in addition to the wall switch and the sensors are located at the normal wall switch location and can be manually overridden.

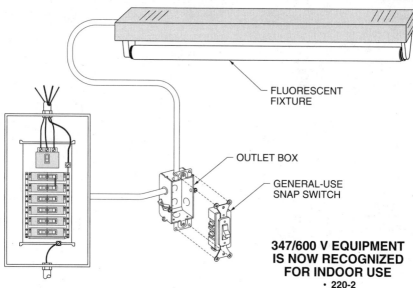

FLUORESCENT
FIXTURE

OUTLET BOX

GENERAL-USE
SNAP SWITCH

**347/600 V EQUIPMENT
IS NOW RECOGNIZED
FOR INDOOR USE**
• 220-2

BRANCH-CIRCUIT, FEEDER,
AND SERVICE CALCULATIONS

220-2

REVISION

In an effort to further harmonize the NEC® with the Canadian Electrical Code, 347 V and 347/600 V have been added to the list of nominal voltages.

CONTINUOUS LOADS – BRANCH CIRCUITS • 220-3(a)

What is the minimum size THW Cu conductor and the minimum size OCPD required for a 100 A continuous load?

Conductor
220-3(a): 100 A x 125% = 125 A
Table 310-16: 125 A = #1
Conductor = **#1 THW Cu**

OCPD
220-3(a): 100 A CB x 125% = 125 A
240-6: 125 A = Standard size
OCPD = **125 A**

BRANCH-CIRCUIT, FEEDER,
AND SERVICE CALCULATIONS

220-3(a)

REVISION

The overcurrent device and conductors shall be derated. Branch circuit conductors shall be sized, without ampacity correction factors, so that their ampacity is equal to or greater than the continuous load plus 125% of the noncontinuous load.

CONTINUOUS LOADS – FEEDER CIRCUITS • 220-10(b)

What is the minimum size THW Cu conductor and the minimum size OCPD required for a 200 A continuous load?

Conductor
220-10(b): 200 A x 125% = 250 A
Table 310-16: 250 A = 250 kcmil
Conductor = **250 kcmil THW Cu**

OCPD
220-10(b): 200 A CB x 125% = 250 A
240-6: 250 A = Standard size
OCPD = **250 A**

BRANCH-CIRCUIT, FEEDER,
AND SERVICE CALCULATIONS

220-10(b)

REVISION

A new second sentence has been added which requires that, like the branch circuit conductors in 220-3(a), feeders and service conductors supplying continuous loads shall have both the overcurrent devices and conductors sized at 125%.

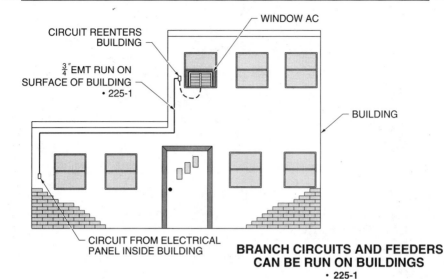

CIRCUIT REENTERS BUILDING

WINDOW AC

$\frac{3}{4}''$ EMT RUN ON SURFACE OF BUILDING • 225-1

BUILDING

CIRCUIT FROM ELECTRICAL PANEL INSIDE BUILDING

BRANCH CIRCUITS AND FEEDERS CAN BE RUN ON BUILDINGS
• 225-1

OUTSIDE BRANCH CIRCUITS AND FEEDERS

225-1

REVISION

The scope of 225 has been revised to included branch circuits or feeders that are run on, not just between, buildings or structures. This revision covers circuits that originate in the inside of a building or structure, leave the building, and then reenter the same building.

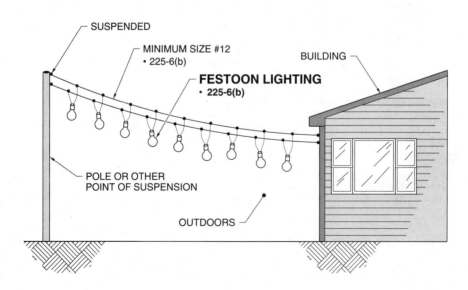

SUSPENDED

MINIMUM SIZE #12 • 225-6(b)

BUILDING

FESTOON LIGHTING
• **225-6(b)**

POLE OR OTHER POINT OF SUSPENSION

OUTDOORS

OUTSIDE BRANCH CIRCUITS AND FEEDERS

225-6(b)

REVISION

The definition of festoon lighting has been revised by removing the 15′ spacing requirement for lampholders. *Festoon lighting* is a string of outdoor lights suspended between two points.

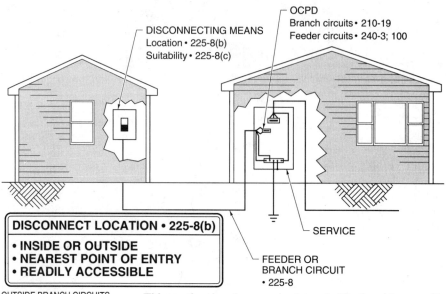

OCPD
Branch circuits• 210-19
Feeder circuits• 240-3; 100

DISCONNECTING MEANS
Location • 225-8(b)
Suitability • 225-8(c)

DISCONNECT LOCATION • 225-8(b)

• **INSIDE OR OUTSIDE**
• **NEAREST POINT OF ENTRY**
• **READILY ACCESSIBLE**

SERVICE

FEEDER OR
BRANCH CIRCUIT
• 225-8

OUTSIDE BRANCH CIRCUITS
AND FEEDERS

225-8(b)

REVISION

This section has been revised to clarify that where a disconnecting means is required at each building or structure served, it shall be installed either inside or outside of the building served, at a readily accessible location where the conductors enter the building.

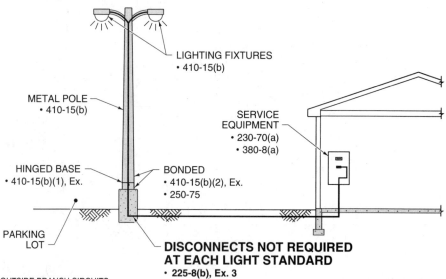

LIGHTING FIXTURES
• 410-15(b)

METAL POLE
• 410-15(b)

SERVICE
EQUIPMENT
• 230-70(a)
• 380-8(a)

HINGED BASE
• 410-15(b)(1), Ex.

BONDED
• 410-15(b)(2), Ex.
• 250-75

PARKING
LOT

**DISCONNECTS NOT REQUIRED
AT EACH LIGHT STANDARD**
• **225-8(b), Ex. 3**

OUTSIDE BRANCH CIRCUITS
AND FEEDERS

225-8(b), Ex. 3

NEW EXCEPTION

A new exception has been added to clarify that for the purposes of 225-8(b), parking lot lighting standards do not constitute a building or structure and a disconnect need not be installed at each lighting pole.

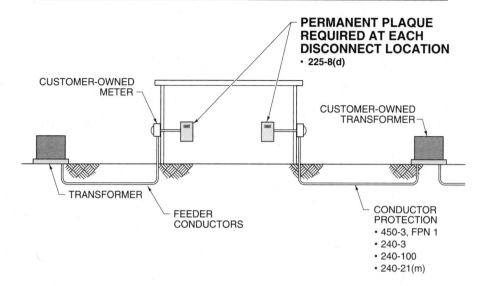

PERMANENT PLAQUE REQUIRED AT EACH DISCONNECT LOCATION
• 225-8(d)

CUSTOMER-OWNED METER

CUSTOMER-OWNED TRANSFORMER

TRANSFORMER

FEEDER CONDUCTORS

CONDUCTOR PROTECTION
• 450-3, FPN 1
• 240-3
• 240-100
• 240-21(m)

OUTSIDE BRANCH CIRCUITS AND FEEDERS

225-8(d)

NEW SECTION

This section requires that where a building or structure is supplied by more than one branch circuit, feeder, or service, a plaque or directory shall be permanently installed at each disconnecting means location specifying all of the other circuits supplying the building and the area they each serve.

OUTSIDE BRANCH CIRCUITS AND FEEDERS

225-8(d), Ex. 1

NEW EXCEPTION

An exception has been added to this new section which removes the requirement for a permanent plaque or directory at each disconnecting means if the building served by more than one branch circuit is a large capacity multibuilding industrial installation, is under single management, and measures are taken to ensure safe switching procedures.

OUTSIDE BRANCH CIRCUITS AND FEEDERS

225-8(d), Ex. 2

NEW EXCEPTION

An exception has been added to this new section which removes the requirement for a permanent plaque or directory if only branch circuits are installed between a dwelling unit and a building or structure.

3' MINIMUM

OPENABLE
WINDOWS

BALCONY

FINAL SPANS • 225-19(d)

INCLUDES:
- **OPENABLE WINDOWS**
- **DOORS**
- **PORCHES**
- **BALCONIES**
- **LADDERS**
- **STAIRS**
- **FIRE ESCAPES**

OUTSIDE BRANCH CIRCUITS
AND FEEDERS

225-19(d)

REVISION

The requirements for final spans of feeders or branch circuits has been revised to specify that the 3' clearance is required only from windows that are designed to be opened. Balconies, ladders, and stairs have been added to the list of items requiring the 3' clearance.

SERVICES

230-2(a)(b)

REVISION

Section 230-2 has been split into two subparts. Part (a) (Number) contains the general rule that each building or structure be served by only one service. The seven exceptions to this rule remain unchanged. Part (b) (Identification) contains the same requirements found in 225-8(d) for installing a permanent plaque or directory when a building or structure is served by more than one service.

SERVICES

230-7

REVISION

This section has been revised by the addition of bonding jumpers to Ex. 1. This revision was necessary to cover installations where the service conductors are installed in FMC and are required by 230-43(15) and 250-79 to be installed with an equipment bonding jumper.

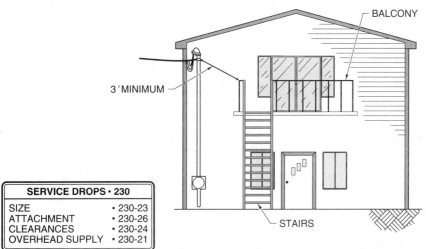

SERVICE DROPS • 230	
SIZE	• 230-23
ATTACHMENT	• 230-26
CLEARANCES	• 230-24
OVERHEAD SUPPLY	• 230-21

BALCONY

3′ MINIMUM

STAIRS

3′ CLEARANCE REQUIREMENTS INCLUDE BALCONIES, LADDERS, AND STAIRS
• 230-9

SERVICES

230-9
REVISION

The list of items that require the 3′ clearance from service conductors has been revised by the addition of balconies, ladders, and stairs.

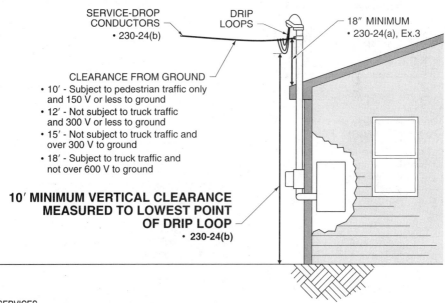

SERVICE-DROP CONDUCTORS
• 230-24(b)

DRIP LOOPS

18″ MINIMUM
• 230-24(a), Ex.3

CLEARANCE FROM GROUND
• 10′ - Subject to pedestrian traffic only and 150 V or less to ground
• 12′ - Not subject to truck traffic and 300 V or less to ground
• 15′ - Not subject to truck traffic and over 300 V to ground
• 18′ - Subject to truck traffic and not over 600 V to ground

10′ MINIMUM VERTICAL CLEARANCE MEASURED TO LOWEST POINT OF DRIP LOOP
• 230-24(b)

SERVICES

230-24(b)
REVISION

The vertical clearance from ground requirement for service-drop conductors has been revised to clarify that the 10′ clearance includes the lowest point of the drip loop.

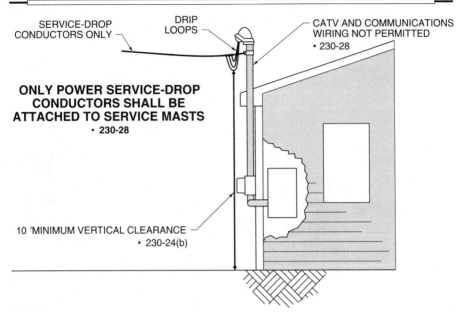

SERVICE-DROP CONDUCTORS ONLY

DRIP LOOPS

CATV AND COMMUNICATIONS WIRING NOT PERMITTED
• 230-28

ONLY POWER SERVICE-DROP CONDUCTORS SHALL BE ATTACHED TO SERVICE MASTS
• **230-28**

10 'MINIMUM VERTICAL CLEARANCE
• 230-24(b)

SERVICES

230-28

REVISION

The FPN following this section has been deleted and the wording has been incorporated into the general rule. Only power service-drop conductors shall be attached to the service mast.

IGS CABLE • 325	
DEFINITION	• 325-1
USES PERMITTED	• 325-3
USES NOT PERMITTED	• 325-4
AMPACITY	• 325-14

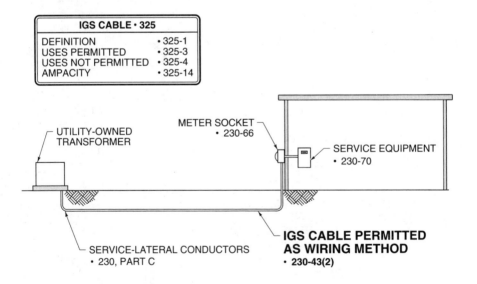

METER SOCKET
• 230-66

UTILITY-OWNED TRANSFORMER

SERVICE EQUIPMENT
• 230-70

IGS CABLE PERMITTED AS WIRING METHOD
• 230-43(2)

SERVICE-LATERAL CONDUCTORS
• 230, PART C

SERVICES

230-43(2)

REVISION

Integrated gas spacer cable (IGS) has been added to the list of permissible wiring methods for service-entrance conductors of 600 V or less.

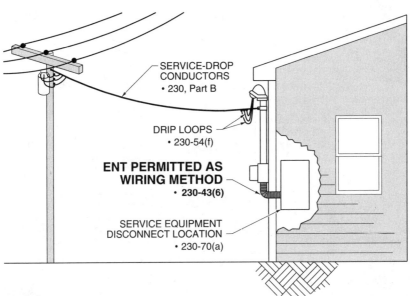

SERVICES

230-43(6)

REVISION

Electrical nonmetallic tubing (ENT) has been added to the list of permissible wiring methods for service-entrance conductors of 600 V or less.

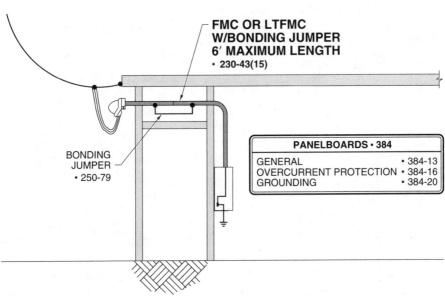

SERVICES

230-43(15)

REVISION

The requirements for FMC and LTFMC have been revised to clarify that the 6′ limitation on length and the bonding jumper requirement apply to both wiring methods.

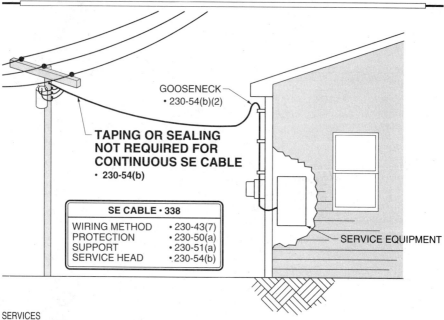

GOOSENECK
• 230-54(b)(2)

TAPING OR SEALING
NOT REQUIRED FOR
CONTINUOUS SE CABLE
• 230-54(b)

SE CABLE • 338	
WIRING METHOD	• 230-43(7)
PROTECTION	• 230-50(a)
SUPPORT	• 230-51(a)
SERVICE HEAD	• 230-54(b)

SERVICE EQUIPMENT

SERVICES

230-54(b)

REVISION

This section has been editorially revised to clarify that if service cables are continuous from the pole to the service equipment, then taping or sealing is not required.

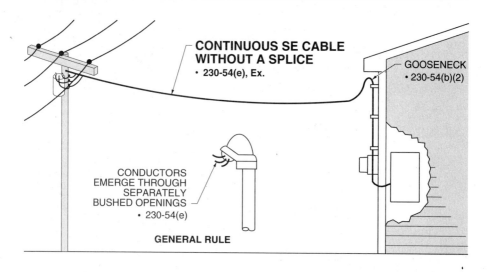

CONTINUOUS SE CABLE
WITHOUT A SPLICE
• 230-54(e), Ex.

GOOSENECK
• 230-54(b)(2)

CONDUCTORS
EMERGE THROUGH
SEPARATELY
BUSHED OPENINGS
• 230-54(e)

GENERAL RULE

SERVICES

230-54(e), Ex.

NEW EXCEPTION

The general rule requires that conductors, of different potential, emerge from service heads through separate openings. The new exception applies to jacketed multiconductor service cables that are installed without a splice, such as when the conductors are run continuously from the pole to the service equipment.

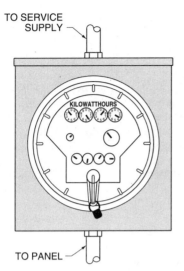

TO SERVICE SUPPLY

KILOWATTHOURS

TO PANEL

**METER SOCKETS ARE
NOT SERVICE EQUIPMENT**
• **230-66**

METER SOCKETS	
GROUNDING	• 230-94, Ex. 5
SPLICES	• 230-46, Ex. 1
OVERHEAD SUPPLY	• 230-21
BONDING	• 250-71(a)(2)

SERVICES

230-66

REVISION

The requirement for marking of service equipment has been revised to specify that it applies only to service equipment rated at 600 V or less. In addition, the FPN following the section has been deleted and the requirement that meter enclosures are not service equipment has been added to the general rule.

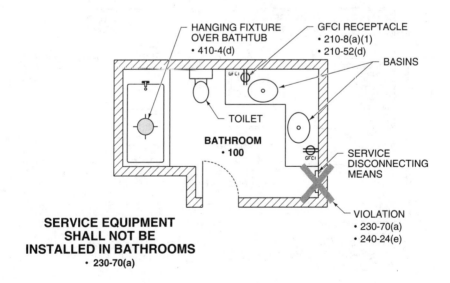

HANGING FIXTURE
OVER BATHTUB
• 410-4(d)

GFCI RECEPTACLE
• 210-8(a)(1)
• 210-52(d)

BASINS

TOILET

BATHROOM
• 100

SERVICE
DISCONNECTING
MEANS

VIOLATION
• 230-70(a)
• 240-24(e)

**SERVICE EQUIPMENT
SHALL NOT BE
INSTALLED IN BATHROOMS**
• **230-70(a)**

SERVICES

230-70(a)

REVISION

This section has been revised to prohibit the installation of service equipment in bathrooms.

230-80

REVISION

After initially voting to delete this section, CMP-4 decided to revise the section to clarify that when multiple service disconnects are installed per 230-71, the combined rating of the disconnecting means shall not be less than the rating required by 230-79. The general rule of 230-79 requires that the service disconnecting means be sized for the load.

230-90(a), Ex. 5

NEW EXCEPTION

This exception correlates Note 3 of Notes to Ampacity Tables of 0 to 2000 Volts to the general rule of 230-90, which requires overcurrent protection for each ungrounded conductor set not higher than the permitted ampacity of the conductor.

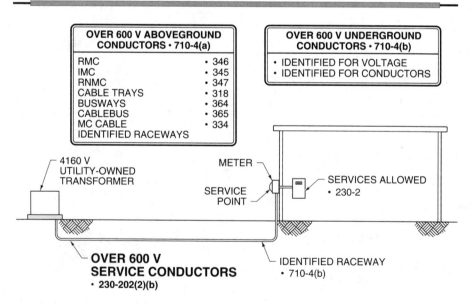

OVER 600 V ABOVEGROUND CONDUCTORS • 710-4(a)	
RMC	• 346
IMC	• 345
RNMC	• 347
CABLE TRAYS	• 318
BUSWAYS	• 364
CABLEBUS	• 365
MC CABLE	• 334
IDENTIFIED RACEWAYS	

OVER 600 V UNDERGROUND CONDUCTORS • 710-4(b)
• IDENTIFIED FOR VOLTAGE
• IDENTIFIED FOR CONDUCTORS

4160 V
UTILITY-OWNED
TRANSFORMER

METER

SERVICE
POINT

SERVICES ALLOWED
• 230-2

OVER 600 V
SERVICE CONDUCTORS
• 230-202(2)(b)

IDENTIFIED RACEWAY
• 710-4(b)

230-202(b)

REVISION

The list of wiring methods permitted for the installation of service conductors exceeding 600 V nominal has been deleted. Instead, the section now references 710-4 which contains the list of permitted wiring methods for conductors over 600 V nominal.

SELECTING OCPDs

Two #4 THW Cu conductors feed an appliance from an individual branch circuit. What is the maximum size standard CB permitted to protect this circuit?

Table 310-16: #4 Cu = 85 A
240-6; 240-3(b): Next higher standard size = 90 A
CB = **90 A**

CONDITION 1 • 240-3(b)

Conductors are not part of more than one outlet branch circuit that supplies cord-and-plug connected loads.

CONDITION 2 • 240-3(b)

Ampacity doesn't correspond with standard ampere ratings per 240-6.

CONDITION 3 • 240-3(b)

Next higher standard rating does not exceed 800 A.

**NEXT HIGHER OCPD
SHALL BE USED**
• 240-3(b)

OVERCURRENT PROTECTION

240-3(b)

REVISION

This section has been revised to clarify the three conditions that shall be met if the next higher standard overcurrent device is to be used. All three of the conditions shall be met to round up to the next higher standard rating.

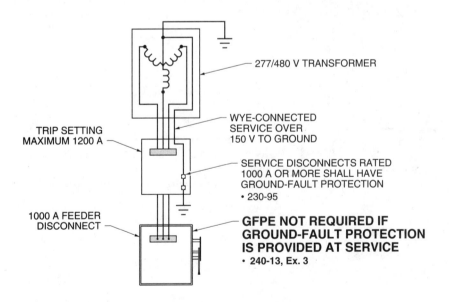

277/480 V TRANSFORMER

WYE-CONNECTED SERVICE OVER 150 V TO GROUND

TRIP SETTING MAXIMUM 1200 A

SERVICE DISCONNECTS RATED 1000 A OR MORE SHALL HAVE GROUND-FAULT PROTECTION
• 230-95

1000 A FEEDER DISCONNECT

GFPE NOT REQUIRED IF GROUND-FAULT PROTECTION IS PROVIDED AT SERVICE
• 240-13, Ex. 3

OVERCURRENT PROTECTION

240-13, Ex. 3

REVISION

Ex. 3 has been revised to clarify that GFPE is not required if the protection is already provided by the feeder or service GFPE.

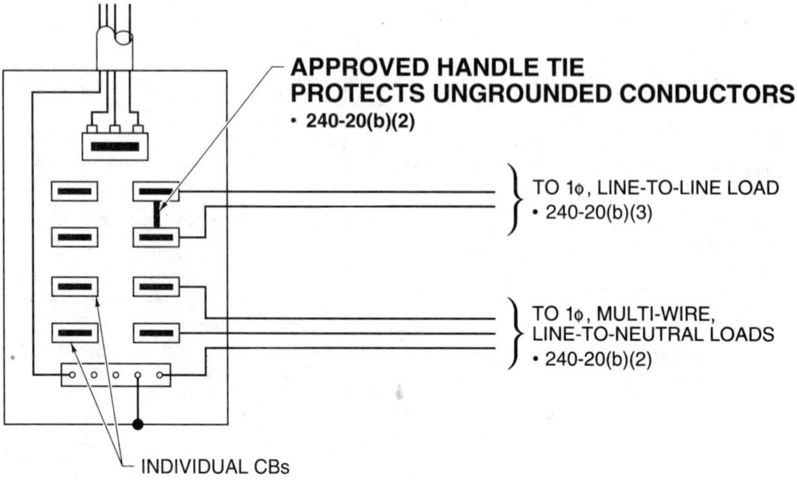

APPROVED HANDLE TIE
PROTECTS UNGROUNDED CONDUCTORS
• 240-20(b)(2)

} TO 1φ, LINE-TO-LINE LOAD
• 240-20(b)(3)

} TO 1φ, MULTI-WIRE,
LINE-TO-NEUTRAL LOADS
• 240-20(b)(2)

INDIVIDUAL CBs

OVERCURRENT PROTECTION

240-20(b)(1)

REVISION

For multiwire branch circuits that serve only 1φ, line-to-neutral loads, individual SPCBs are permitted to be installed either with or without handle ties for protection of the ungrounded conductors.

OVERCURRENT PROTECTION

240-20(b)(2)

REVISION

For line-to-line, 1φ circuits or 3-wire, DC circuits, individual SPCBs with handle ties are permitted for the protection of the ungrounded conductors.

OVERCURRENT PROTECTION

240-20(b)(3)

REVISION

Individual SPCBs with approved handle ties are permitted for the protection of ungrounded conductors for line-to-line 3φ, 4-wire or 2φ, 5-wire grounded systems.

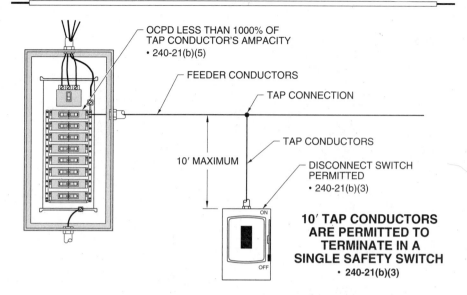

OCPD LESS THAN 1000% OF TAP CONDUCTOR'S AMPACITY
• 240-21(b)(5)

FEEDER CONDUCTORS

TAP CONNECTION

TAP CONDUCTORS

10′ MAXIMUM

DISCONNECT SWITCH PERMITTED
• 240-21(b)(3)

10′ TAP CONDUCTORS ARE PERMITTED TO TERMINATE IN A SINGLE SAFETY SWITCH
• **240-21(b)(3)**

OVERCURRENT PROTECTION

240-21(b)(3)

REVISION

The provision of the 10′ tap rule covering tap conductor termination has been revised by the addition of "disconnecting means" as a permissible termination point for the tap conductors. This clarifies that 10′ tap conductors are permitted to terminate in a single safety switch.

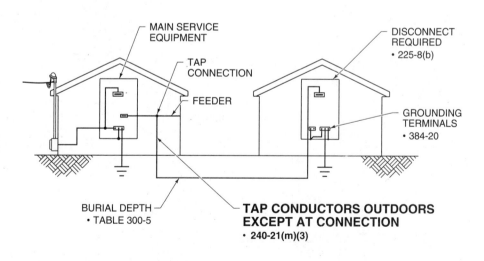

MAIN SERVICE EQUIPMENT

DISCONNECT REQUIRED
• 225-8(b)

TAP CONNECTION

FEEDER

GROUNDING TERMINALS
• 384-20

BURIAL DEPTH
• TABLE 300-5

TAP CONDUCTORS OUTDOORS EXCEPT AT CONNECTION
• **240-21(m)(3)**

OVERCURRENT PROTECTION

240-21(m)(3)

NEW SUBSECTION

A new subsection has been added to the requirements for outdoor feeder taps. This subsection requires that, except at the point of termination, the tap conductors shall be installed outdoors.

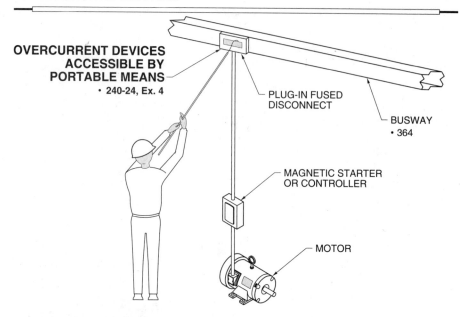

OVERCURRENT DEVICES ACCESSIBLE BY PORTABLE MEANS
• 240-24, Ex. 4

PLUG-IN FUSED DISCONNECT

BUSWAY
• 364

MAGNETIC STARTER OR CONTROLLER

MOTOR

OVERCURRENT PROTECTION

240-24, Ex. 4

NEW EXCEPTION

This exception permits overcurrent devices, installed next to motors and other equipment, to be accessible by portable means. This exception correlates with similar provisions in 380-8(a), Ex. 2.

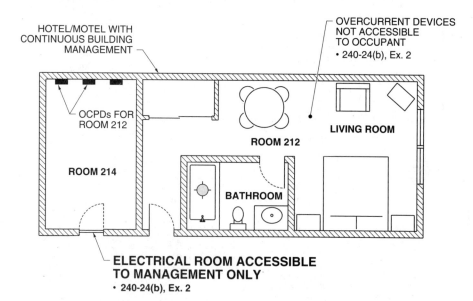

HOTEL/MOTEL WITH CONTINUOUS BUILDING MANAGEMENT

OVERCURRENT DEVICES NOT ACCESSIBLE TO OCCUPANT
• 240-24(b), Ex. 2

OCPDs FOR ROOM 212

LIVING ROOM

ROOM 212

ROOM 214

BATHROOM

ELECTRICAL ROOM ACCESSIBLE TO MANAGEMENT ONLY
• 240-24(b), Ex. 2

OVERCURRENT PROTECTION

240-24(b), Ex. 2

NEW EXCEPTION

This exception permits OCPDs to be installed in a location that is only accessible to management, provided the occupancy is a hotel or motel and building management supervision is continuous.

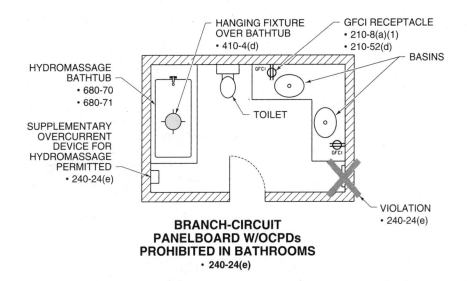

HANGING FIXTURE
OVER BATHTUB
• 410-4(d)

GFCI RECEPTACLE
• 210-8(a)(1)
• 210-52(d)

BASINS

HYDROMASSAGE
BATHTUB
• 680-70
• 680-71

SUPPLEMENTARY
OVERCURRENT
DEVICE FOR
HYDROMASSAGE
PERMITTED
• 240-24(e)

TOILET

VIOLATION
• 240-24(e)

**BRANCH-CIRCUIT
PANELBOARD W/OCPDs
PROHIBITED IN BATHROOMS**
• **240-24(e)**

OVERCURRENT PROTECTION

240-24(e)

REVISION

The section has been revised to clarify that, with the exception of supplementary devices, all OCPDs are prohibited from being installed in bathrooms.

OVERCURRENT PROTECTION

240-83(d)

REVISION

The section has been revised to clarify that CBs, when used as switches, shall be listed and shall contain the marking "SWD."

OVERCURRENT PROTECTION

240-85

NEW SECTION

The FPN that followed 240-83(e) has been deleted and the identical text now appears as 240-85. The reason stated is that the information contained in the FPN is a safety concern that is directly related to the listing.

GROUNDING

250-24(a), Ex. 2
REVISION

Ex. 2 has been revised to clarify that whenever a building is supplied from a service in another building, by more than one branch circuit, a grounding electrode shall be installed at the second building.

GROUNDING

250-26(c)
REVISION

The requirements for the GEC for a separately derived system have been revised to clarify that the connection to the grounding electrode is to be made in the same area as the GEC connection to the system, not the equipment grounding conductor connection.

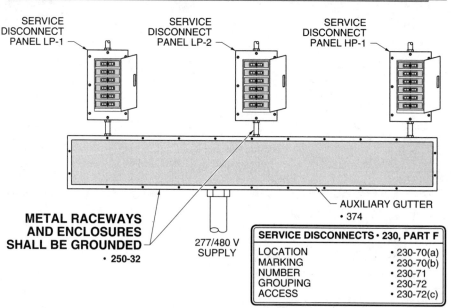

SERVICE DISCONNECT PANEL LP-1

SERVICE DISCONNECT PANEL LP-2

SERVICE DISCONNECT PANEL HP-1

AUXILIARY GUTTER
• 374

METAL RACEWAYS AND ENCLOSURES SHALL BE GROUNDED
• 250-32

277/480 V SUPPLY

SERVICE DISCONNECTS • 230, PART F	
LOCATION	• 230-70(a)
MARKING	• 230-70(b)
NUMBER	• 230-71
GROUPING	• 230-72
ACCESS	• 230-72(c)

GROUNDING

250-32
REVISION

The title of this section and the text have been modified to require that raceways and enclosures both shall be grounded. A similar change has occurred in 250-33 and 250-33, Ex. 1 and 2 for enclosures and raceways for other conductors.

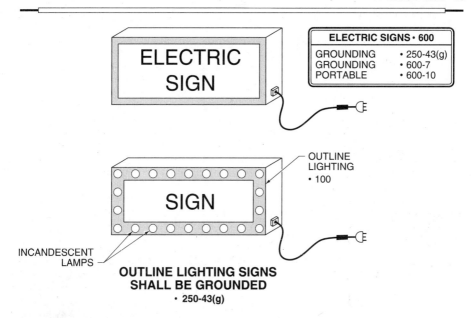

ELECTRIC SIGNS · 600

GROUNDING	• 250-43(g)
GROUNDING	• 600-7
PORTABLE	• 600-10

OUTLINE LIGHTING · 100

INCANDESCENT LAMPS

OUTLINE LIGHTING SIGNS SHALL BE GROUNDED
• 250-43(g)

GROUNDING

250-43(g)
REVISION

The requirement for grounding electric signs has been expanded to include outline lighting.

GROUNDING

250-44(a)
REVISION

The grounding requirement for frames and tracks of electrically operated cranes has been revised to include electrically operated hoists.

GROUNDING

250-46
REVISION

The 6′ spacing of lightning rod conductors from other metal equipment, enclosures, raceways, etc., has been clarified to require that the two shall be bonded not simply at any convenient location but at the point where the two systems are less than 6′ apart.

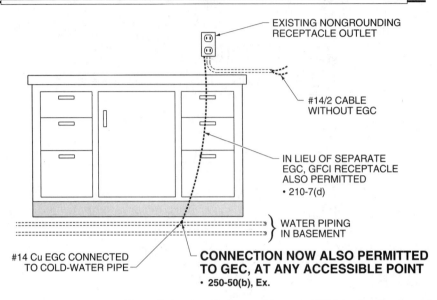

EXISTING NONGROUNDING
RECEPTACLE OUTLET

#14/2 CABLE
WITHOUT EGC

IN LIEU OF SEPARATE
EGC, GFCI RECEPTACLE
ALSO PERMITTED
• 210-7(d)

} WATER PIPING
  IN BASEMENT

#14 Cu EGC CONNECTED
TO COLD-WATER PIPE

**CONNECTION NOW ALSO PERMITTED
TO GEC, AT ANY ACCESSIBLE POINT**
• 250-50(b), Ex.

GROUNDING

250-50(b), Ex.

REVISION

For existing installations, without an EGC in the circuit, and in which a grounding receptacle is used to replace a nongrounding receptacle, the grounding connection is permitted to be any accessible point in the grounding electrode system or any accessible point on the grounding electrode conductor.

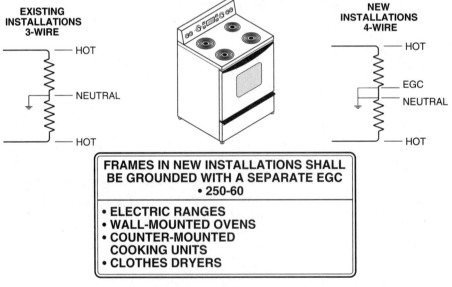

EXISTING
INSTALLATIONS
3-WIRE

HOT

NEUTRAL

HOT

NEW
INSTALLATIONS
4-WIRE

HOT

EGC
NEUTRAL

HOT

**FRAMES IN NEW INSTALLATIONS SHALL
BE GROUNDED WITH A SEPARATE EGC**
• 250-60

• **ELECTRIC RANGES**
• **WALL-MOUNTED OVENS**
• **COUNTER-MOUNTED
  COOKING UNITS**
• **CLOTHES DRYERS**

GROUNDING

250-60

REVISION

The longstanding permission to install 3-wire circuits to ranges, wall-mounted ovens, counter-mounted cooking units and dryers has been revised to limit this permission only to existing branch-circuits. In new installations, the frames of these appliances shall be grounded per 250-57 or 250-59.

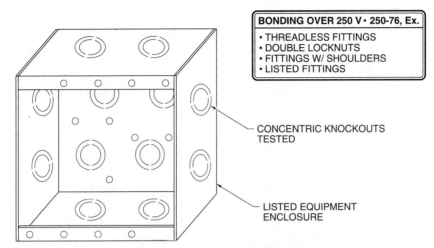

CONCENTRIC KNOCKOUTS TESTED

LISTED EQUIPMENT ENCLOSURE

GROUNDING NOT REQUIRED FOR CIRCUITS OVER 250 V TO GROUND WHEN KNOCKOUTS HAVE BEEN TESTED AND BOX IS LISTED
• 250-76, Ex.

GROUNDING

250-76, Ex.

REVISION

The exception for bonding over 250 V has been revised to remove the necessity for bonding around concentric or eccentric knockouts when the knockouts have been tested and the box is listed for the use.

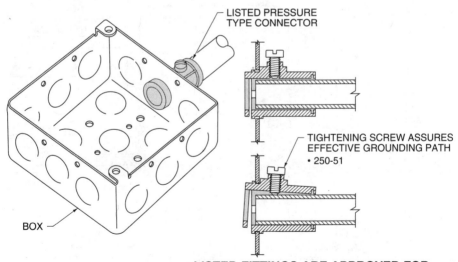

LISTED PRESSURE TYPE CONNECTOR

TIGHTENING SCREW ASSURES EFFECTIVE GROUNDING PATH
• 250-51

BOX

LISTED FITTINGS ARE APPROVED FOR BONDING CIRCUITS OVER 250 V TO GROUND
• 250-76, Ex. (d)

GROUNDING

250-76, Ex. (d)

NEW SUBSECTION

A new subpart (d) has been added to (d) the existing exception to permit the use of listed fittings as a means to satisfy the over 250 V bonding requirement in the general rule.

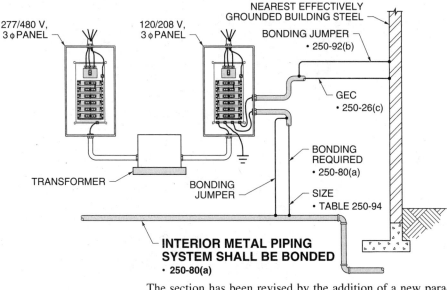

277/480 V, 3φ PANEL

120/208 V, 3φ PANEL

NEAREST EFFECTIVELY GROUNDED BUILDING STEEL

BONDING JUMPER
• 250-92(b)

GEC
• 250-26(c)

BONDING REQUIRED
• 250-80(a)

SIZE
• TABLE 250-94

TRANSFORMER

BONDING JUMPER

INTERIOR METAL PIPING SYSTEM SHALL BE BONDED
• 250-80(a)

GROUNDING

250-80(a)

REVISION

The section has been revised by the addition of a new paragraph which requires that when separately derived systems are installed, the interior metal water piping, nearest the area served, shall be bonded to the grounded conductor of the separately derived system.

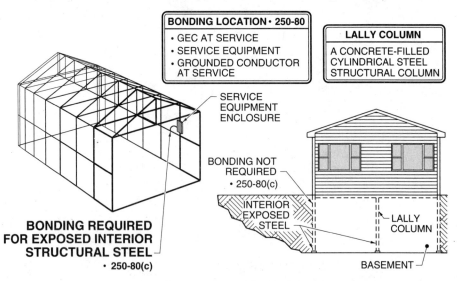

BONDING LOCATION • 250-80
• GEC AT SERVICE
• SERVICE EQUIPMENT
• GROUNDED CONDUCTOR AT SERVICE

LALLY COLUMN
A CONCRETE-FILLED CYLINDRICAL STEEL STRUCTURAL COLUMN

SERVICE EQUIPMENT ENCLOSURE

BONDING NOT REQUIRED
• 250-80(c)

INTERIOR EXPOSED STEEL

LALLY COLUMN

BASEMENT

BONDING REQUIRED FOR EXPOSED INTERIOR STRUCTURAL STEEL
• 250-80(c)

GROUNDING

250-80(c)

NEW SUBSECTION

A new subsection has been added covering the bonding of exposed interior structural steel. Steel, that is not intentionally grounded and is likely to become energized, is required to be bonded to the service equipment enclosure, the grounded conductor, or the GEC at the service or to the grounding electrodes themselves.

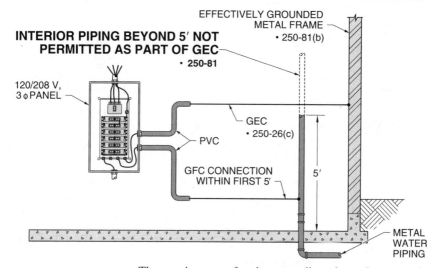

INTERIOR PIPING BEYOND 5′ NOT PERMITTED AS PART OF GEC
• **250-81**

EFFECTIVELY GROUNDED METAL FRAME
• 250-81(b)

120/208 V, 3 φ PANEL

GEC
• 250-26(c)

PVC

GFC CONNECTION WITHIN FIRST 5′

5′

METAL WATER PIPING

The requirements for the grounding electrode system have been revised. The provision dealing with interior metal water piping has been rewritten to clarify that piping located beyond the first 5′ of the entrance to the building shall not be used as a conductor to interconnect components of the grounding electrode system nor shall it be used as a part of the grounding electrode system.

GROUNDING

250-81

REVISION

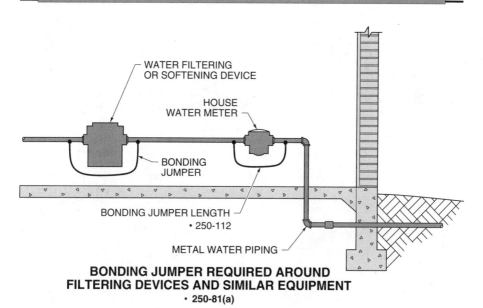

WATER FILTERING OR SOFTENING DEVICE

HOUSE WATER METER

BONDING JUMPER

BONDING JUMPER LENGTH
• 250-112

METAL WATER PIPING

BONDING JUMPER REQUIRED AROUND FILTERING DEVICES AND SIMILAR EQUIPMENT
• 250-81(a)

GROUNDING

250-81(a)

REVISION

The provisions for bonding of metal piping components that may affect the integrity of the grounding electrode system have been revised to include filtering devices and similar equipment along with water meters.

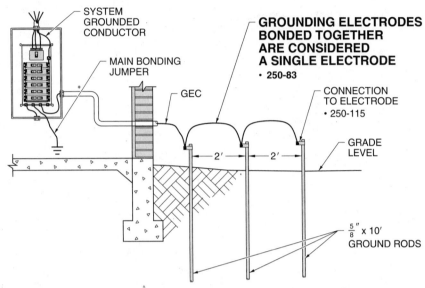

SYSTEM GROUNDED CONDUCTOR

MAIN BONDING JUMPER

GEC

GROUNDING ELECTRODES BONDED TOGETHER ARE CONSIDERED A SINGLE ELECTRODE
• 250-83

CONNECTION TO ELECTRODE
• 250-115

GRADE LEVEL

2′ 2′

$\frac{5}{8}''$ x 10′ GROUND RODS

GROUNDING

250-83

REVISION

The FPN that followed this section has been incorporated into the last sentence of the general rule. If the grounding electrodes are bonded together, they shall be considered a single system.

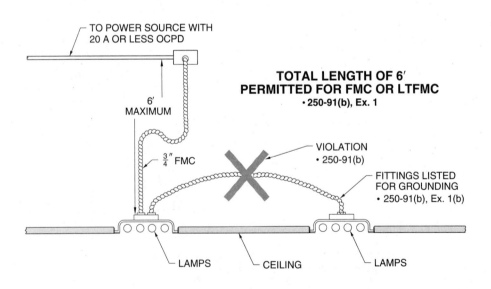

TO POWER SOURCE WITH 20 A OR LESS OCPD

6′ MAXIMUM

$\frac{3}{4}''$ FMC

TOTAL LENGTH OF 6′ PERMITTED FOR FMC OR LTFMC
• 250-91(b), Ex. 1

VIOLATION
• 250-91(b)

FITTINGS LISTED FOR GROUNDING
• 250-91(b), Ex. 1(b)

LAMPS CEILING LAMPS

GROUNDING

250-91(b), Ex. 1

REVISION

The exception has been modified to allow non-listed flexible metal (FMC) conduit to be used for grounding provided the circuit conductors are protected at 20 A or less, the FMC is listed as a raceway, and the fittings are listed for grounding.

GROUNDING

250-91(b), Ex. 2
REVISION

The exception has been revised to clarify the requirements for flexible metal conduit (FMC) and liquidtight flexible metal conduit (LTFMC) in circuits exceeding 20 A but not more than 60 A.

GROUNDING

250-91(b), Ex. 3
DELETION

Ex. 3 has been deleted because it referenced installation provisions that were not covered by 250-91(b).

GROUNDING

250-93, Ex.
NEW EXCEPTION

A new three-part exception that parallels the sizing requirements for AC GECs in 250-94, Ex. permits DC GECs to be reduced in size when they are the sole connection to (a) made electrodes, (b) concrete-encased electrodes, or (c) ground rings.

GROUNDING

250-94, Ex.
REVISION

Ex. 1 and 2 have been combined into a single exception which contains the requirements for both grounded and ungrounded AC systems. The AC GEC shall be no smaller than listed in Table 250-94 except where connected to (a) made electrodes, (b) concrete-encased electrodes, and (c) ground rings.

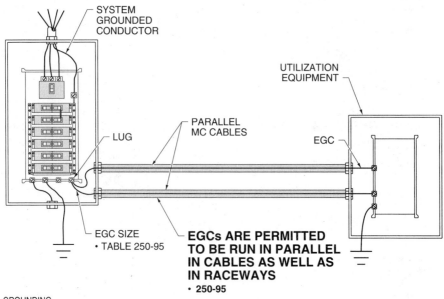

SYSTEM
GROUNDED
CONDUCTOR

UTILIZATION
EQUIPMENT

PARALLEL
MC CABLES

EGC

LUG

EGC SIZE
• TABLE 250-95

**EGCs ARE PERMITTED
TO BE RUN IN PARALLEL
IN CABLES AS WELL AS
IN RACEWAYS**
• **250-95**

GROUNDING

250-95

REVISION

This section has been revised to clarify that the same rule for sizing EGCs applies whether the conductors are run in parallel raceways or parallel cables.

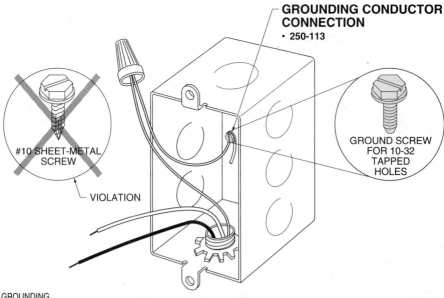

**GROUNDING CONDUCTOR
CONNECTION**
• **250-113**

#10 SHEET-METAL
SCREW

VIOLATION

GROUND SCREW
FOR 10-32
TAPPED
HOLES

GROUNDING

250-113

REVISION

The requirements for connection of grounding conductors to enclosures and equipment have been modified to prohibit the use of sheet-metal screws for this purpose.

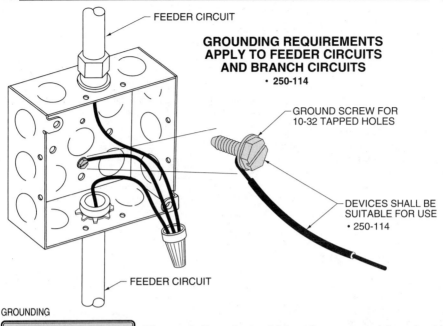

FEEDER CIRCUIT

**GROUNDING REQUIREMENTS
APPLY TO FEEDER CIRCUITS
AND BRANCH CIRCUITS**
• 250-114

GROUND SCREW FOR
10-32 TAPPED HOLES

DEVICES SHALL BE
SUITABLE FOR USE
• 250-114

FEEDER CIRCUIT

GROUNDING

250-114

REVISION

The words "branch-circuit" have been removed from the title of this section to ensure that the requirements of the section apply to feeders and cord sets as well as branch-circuits.

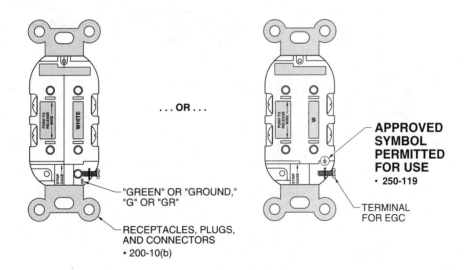

. . . OR . . .

WHITE

PUSH TO RELEASE WIRE

STRIP GAGE

"GREEN" OR "GROUND,"
"G" OR "GR"

RECEPTACLES, PLUGS,
AND CONNECTORS
• 200-10(b)

W

PUSH TO RELEASE WIRE

STRIP GAGE

**APPROVED
SYMBOL
PERMITTED
FOR USE**
• 250-119

TERMINAL
FOR EGC

GROUNDING

250-119

REVISION

The requirements for identifying the terminal for the EGC on wiring devices has been expanded to permit the use of the symbol in lieu of the word "green," or "ground," or the letters "G" or "GR."

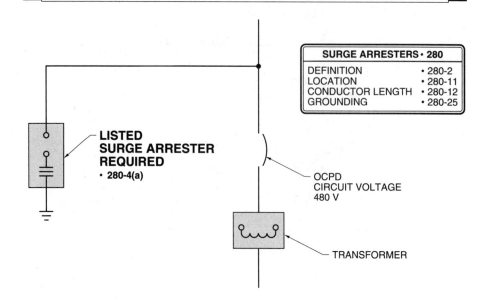

SURGE ARRESTERS · 280	
DEFINITION	• 280-2
LOCATION	• 280-11
CONDUCTOR LENGTH	• 280-12
GROUNDING	• 280-25

LISTED SURGE ARRESTER REQUIRED
• 280-4(a)

OCPD
CIRCUIT VOLTAGE
480 V

TRANSFORMER

SURGE ARRESTERS

280-4(a)

REVISION

The provisions for surge arresters in circuits less than 1000 V have been modified to require that all surge arresters used in circuits of less than 1000 V shall be listed.

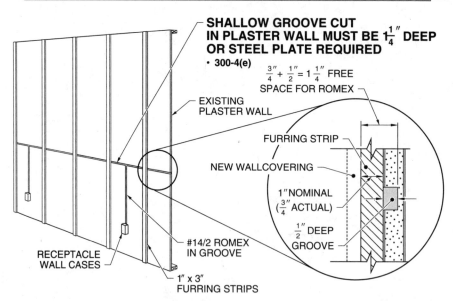

SHALLOW GROOVE CUT IN PLASTER WALL MUST BE $1\frac{1}{4}''$ DEEP OR STEEL PLATE REQUIRED
• 300-4(e)

$\frac{3''}{4} + \frac{1''}{2} = 1\frac{1}{4}''$ FREE SPACE FOR ROMEX

EXISTING PLASTER WALL

FURRING STRIP

NEW WALLCOVERING

1" NOMINAL ($\frac{3''}{4}$ ACTUAL)

$\frac{1''}{2}$ DEEP GROOVE

#14/2 ROMEX IN GROOVE

RECEPTACLE WALL CASES

1" x 3" FURRING STRIPS

WIRING METHODS

300-4(e)

NEW SUBSECTION

A new subsection has been added that requires when cables or raceways are installed in shallow grooves in walls that will be covered with sheetrock, paneling, or similar finishes the cables or raceways shall be protected with $\frac{1}{16}''$ steel plate or equivalent for the entire length.

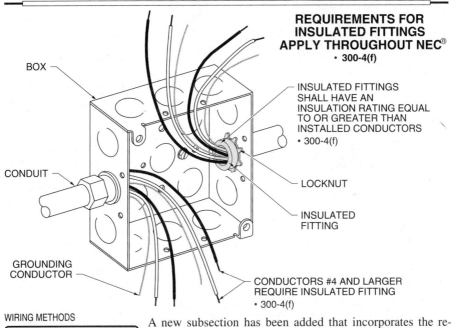

**REQUIREMENTS FOR
INSULATED FITTINGS
APPLY THROUGHOUT NEC®**
• **300-4(f)**

BOX

INSULATED FITTINGS
SHALL HAVE AN
INSULATION RATING EQUAL
TO OR GREATER THAN
INSTALLED CONDUCTORS
• 300-4(f)

CONDUIT

LOCKNUT

INSULATED
FITTING

GROUNDING
CONDUCTOR

CONDUCTORS #4 AND LARGER
REQUIRE INSULATED FITTING
• 300-4(f)

WIRING METHODS

300-4(f)

NEW SUBSECTION

A new subsection has been added that incorporates the requirements found in 373-6(c) into 300, which makes the requirements for insulated fittings apply throughout the NEC®.

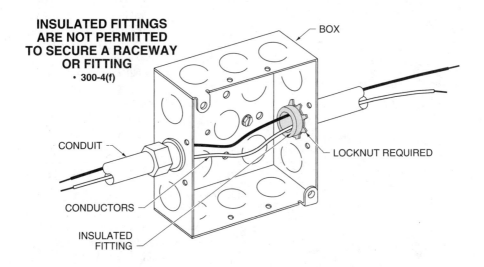

**INSULATED FITTINGS
ARE NOT PERMITTED
TO SECURE A RACEWAY
OR FITTING**
• **300-4(f)**

BOX

CONDUIT

LOCKNUT REQUIRED

CONDUCTORS

INSULATED
FITTING

WIRING METHODS

300-4(f)

NEW SUBSECTION

The new subsection contains a provision that the insulated fittings required by the section shall not be used to secure a fitting or raceway.

WIRING METHODS

Table 300-5

DELETION

The last (bottom) row of the Table covering the requirements for installations in solid rock has been deleted. The requirements now appear in Note 5 to the Table.

WIRING METHODS

300-5(e)

REVISION

The requirements for underground splices and taps have been revised to reference the direct burial splice requirements contained in 110-14(b). Splices underground shall be made with listed wire connectors or methods.

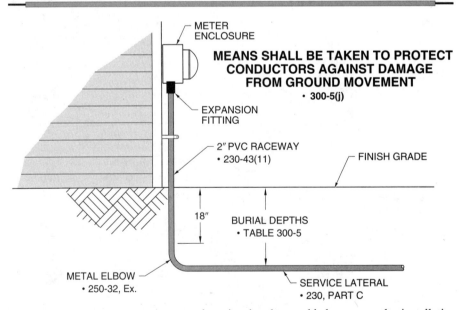

METER ENCLOSURE

MEANS SHALL BE TAKEN TO PROTECT CONDUCTORS AGAINST DAMAGE FROM GROUND MOVEMENT
• 300-5(j)

EXPANSION FITTING

2″ PVC RACEWAY
• 230-43(11)

FINISH GRADE

18″

BURIAL DEPTHS
• TABLE 300-5

METAL ELBOW
• 250-32, Ex.

SERVICE LATERAL
• 230, PART C

WIRING METHODS

300-5(j)

NEW SUBSECTION

A new subsection has been added to cover the installation of cables and raceways in areas subject to ground movement. The requirements state that some means shall be taken to protect against damage to the conductors as a result of ground movement.

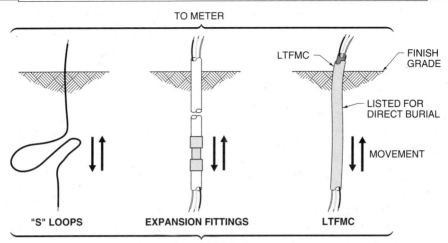

TO METER

"S" LOOPS   EXPANSION FITTINGS   LTFMC

LTFMC — FINISH GRADE

LISTED FOR DIRECT BURIAL

MOVEMENT

TO POWER SOURCE

RACEWAY AND CABLE PROVISIONS FOR LIMITING CONDUCTOR DAMAGE FROM GROUND MOVEMENT
• 300-5(j), FPN

WIRING METHODS

300-5(j), FPN

NEW FPN

A new FPN has been added to the end of the subsection, which lists three specific means to limit the damage to conductors as a result of ground movement. "S" loops, expansion fittings, and flexible connections are listed.

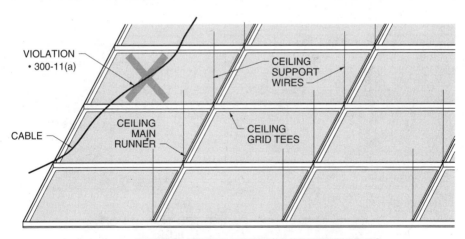

VIOLATION
• 300-11(a)

CEILING SUPPORT WIRES

CABLE

CEILING MAIN RUNNER

CEILING GRID TEES

CEILING GRIDS ARE NOT PERMITTED TO SUPPORT CABLES OR RACEWAYS IN EITHER FIRE- OR NONFIRE-RATED CEILINGS
• 300-11(a)

WIRING METHODS

300-11(a)

REVISION

Ceiling grids, in either fire-rated or nonfire-rated ceiling assemblies are not permitted to support any cables or raceways.

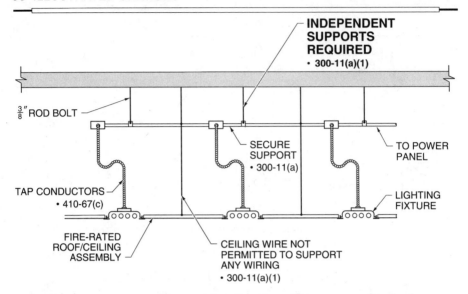

INDEPENDENT
SUPPORTS
REQUIRED
• 300-11(a)(1)

$\frac{3}{8}''$ ROD BOLT

SECURE
SUPPORT
• 300-11(a)

TO POWER
PANEL

TAP CONDUCTORS
• 410-67(c)

LIGHTING
FIXTURE

FIRE-RATED
ROOF/CEILING
ASSEMBLY

CEILING WIRE NOT
PERMITTED TO SUPPORT
ANY WIRING
• 300-11(a)(1)

WIRING METHODS

300-11(a)(1)

REVISION

The provisions for using ceiling support wires for the support of raceways, cable assemblies, boxes, etc., have been modified. For wiring located above fire-rated roof/ceiling/floor assemblies, an independent means of support shall be provided unless the ceiling support system has been tested as part of the fire-rated assembly.

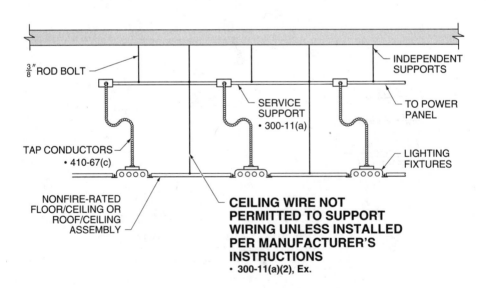

$\frac{3}{8}''$ ROD BOLT

INDEPENDENT
SUPPORTS

SERVICE
SUPPORT
• 300-11(a)

TO POWER
PANEL

TAP CONDUCTORS
• 410-67(c)

LIGHTING
FIXTURES

NONFIRE-RATED
FLOOR/CEILING OR
ROOF/CEILING
ASSEMBLY

**CEILING WIRE NOT
PERMITTED TO SUPPORT
WIRING UNLESS INSTALLED
PER MANUFACTURER'S
INSTRUCTIONS**
• 300-11(a)(2), Ex.

WIRING METHODS

300-11(a)(2)

REVISION

For nonfire-rated floor/ceiling or roof/ceiling assemblies, wiring shall not be supported by the ceiling support wires unless the ceiling system manufacturer's instructions specifically permit the ceiling wires to be used for support.

WIRING METHODS

300-13(a)

REVISION

The five exceptions following this section have been deleted. The provisions contained in the exceptions have been incorporated into the general rule.

WIRING METHODS

300-16

REVISION

ENT has been added to the list of wiring methods that shall use a box or fitting when changing to open wiring or concealed knob-and-tube wiring.

TEMPORARY WIRING

305-2

NEW SUBSECTION

A new subsection has been added that requires all temporary wiring methods to be approved for the conditions of use.

TEMPORARY WIRING

305-3(b)

REVISION

A new 525 has been added that contains all of the provisions for electrical installations in carnivals, circuses, fairs, and similar events. References to carnivals, as found in this section, have been deleted.

TEMPORARY WIRING

305-4(b)
REVISION

The permission to run feeders as open conductors has been removed. Feeders shall be run within cable assemblies, or cords or cables of the hard or extra-hard usage type.

TEMPORARY WIRING

305-4(c)
REVISION

The permission to run branch circuits as open conductors has been removed. Branch circuit conductors shall be installed within cable assemblies, or multiconductor cord or cable of the hard or extra-hard usage type.

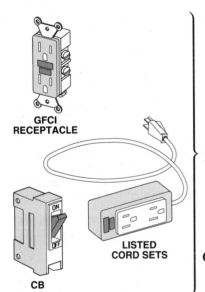

GFCI RECEPTACLE

CB

LISTED CORD SETS

GFCI PROTECTION REQUIRED FOR TEMPORARY WIRING ON:

• **CONSTRUCTION SITES**

• **REMODELING**

• **MAINTENANCE**

• **BUILDING REPAIR**

• **BUILDING DEMOLITION**

GFCI PROTECTION HAS BEEN EXPANDED BEYOND CONSTRUCTION SITES
• 305-6

TEMPORARY WIRING

305-6
REVISION

The requirements for GFCI protection for temporary wiring has been expanded beyond just construction sites. All 15 or 20 A, 125 V receptacles for temporary power for construction, remodeling, maintenance, repair, etc, shall be GFCI protected.

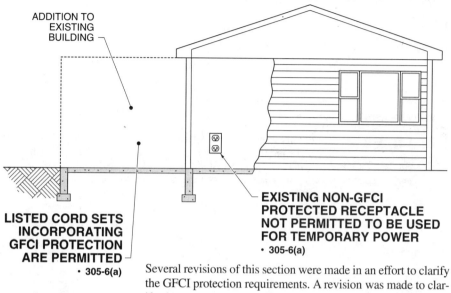

ADDITION TO
EXISTING
BUILDING

**LISTED CORD SETS
INCORPORATING
GFCI PROTECTION
ARE PERMITTED**
• 305-6(a)

**EXISTING NON-GFCI
PROTECTED RECEPTACLE
NOT PERMITTED TO BE USED
FOR TEMPORARY POWER**
• 305-6(a)

TEMPORARY WIRING

305-6(a)

REVISION

Several revisions of this section were made in an effort to clarify the GFCI protection requirements. A revision was made to clarify that any receptacle, whether it is existing or a part of the permanent wiring of the building, shall have GFCI protection if it is used to supply temporary power. In addition, a new sentence was added to clarify that the GFCI protection can be provided in cord sets incorporating listed GFCI protection.

TEMPORARY WIRING

305-6(a), Ex. 2

NEW EXCEPTION

This exception permits qualified personnel, in industrial establishments only, to utilize the assured equipment grounding conductor program (AEGCP) for receptacles other than those covered in subpart (a).

TEMPORARY WIRING

305-6(b)

REVISION

The provisions of the assured equipment grounding conductor program (AEGCP) have been modified to permit the program to be used only for the receptacles not covered by 305-6(a). This limits the programs use to receptacles other than 125 V, 15 or 20 A.

CONDUCTORS
FOR GENERAL WIRING

310-4, Ex. 4

NEW EXCEPTION

This new exception permits, under engineering supervision, the paralleling of #2 and larger neutral conductors to alleviate the overloading of the neutral as a result of harmonics.

CONDUCTORS
FOR GENERAL WIRING

310-4, FPN

REVISION

The FPN following this section has been revised to clarify that the rules for paralleling conductors apply to each set of the parallel conductors but not to all of the sets collectively.

CONDUCTORS
FOR GENERAL WIRING

310-15, FPN

REVISION

The FPN has been revised by referencing 210-19(a), FPN 4 for branch-circuit voltage drop and 215-2(b), FPN 2 for feeder voltage drop.

CONDUCTORS
FOR GENERAL WIRING

Table 310-16

REVISION

The title to Table 310-16 has been revised to indicate that the Table lists allowable ampacities for not more than three *current-carrying* conductors. Note 10 of Notes to Ampacity Tables of 0 to 2000 Volts can be used to determine when the neutral conductor should be considered a current-carrying conductor.

CONDUCTORS
FOR GENERAL WIRING

Table 310-19
REVISION

The bare or covered conductor column for aluminum or copper-clad aluminum conductors has been deleted. The ampacities were, in many cases, lower than the insulated column, yet Note 5 permits the ampacity of bare conductors to be based on those of the adjacent insulated conductors.

CONDUCTORS
FOR GENERAL WIRING

Note 3 of Notes to Ampacity Tables of 0 to 2000 Volts
REVISION

Note 3 has been revised for better clarification and understanding. A new sentence has been added which limits the size of the feeder conductors to a building to the size of the service-entrance conductors.

**CABLE TRAYS PERMITTED
FOR USE IN OTHER THAN
INDUSTRIAL ESTABLISHMENTS**
• 318-3

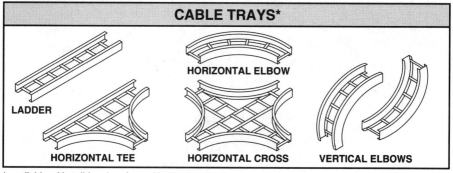

CABLE TRAYS*

LADDER

HORIZONTAL ELBOW

HORIZONTAL TEE   HORIZONTAL CROSS   VERTICAL ELBOWS

* available with solid and perforated bottoms

CABLE TRAYS

318-3
REVISION

This section has been revised by incorporating the existing FPN into the general rule. This clarifies that cable tray systems are permitted to be installed in other than industrial establishments.

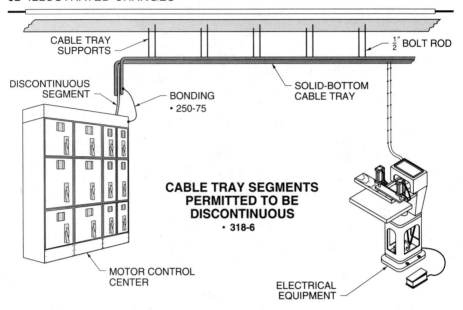

CABLE TRAY
SUPPORTS

$\frac{1}{2}''$ BOLT ROD

DISCONTINUOUS
SEGMENT

BONDING
• 250-75

SOLID-BOTTOM
CABLE TRAY

**CABLE TRAY SEGMENTS
PERMITTED TO BE
DISCONTINUOUS**
• 318-6

MOTOR CONTROL
CENTER

ELECTRICAL
EQUIPMENT

CABLE TRAYS

318-6

REVISION

The FPN following this section has been deleted. The permission to install discontinuous segments between cable tray runs and equipment is now included in the general rule.

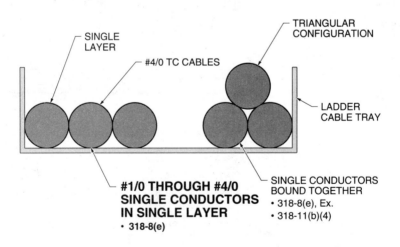

SINGLE
LAYER

TRIANGULAR
CONFIGURATION

#4/0 TC CABLES

LADDER
CABLE TRAY

**#1/0 THROUGH #4/0
SINGLE CONDUCTORS
IN SINGLE LAYER**
• 318-8(e)

SINGLE CONDUCTORS
BOUND TOGETHER
• 318-8(e), Ex.
• 318-11(b)(4)

CABLE TRAYS

318-8(e)

NEW SUBSECTION

A new subsection covering the installation of single conductors in cable tray systems has been added. In addition, an exception to the general rule permits single conductors to be bound together per 318-11(b)(4).

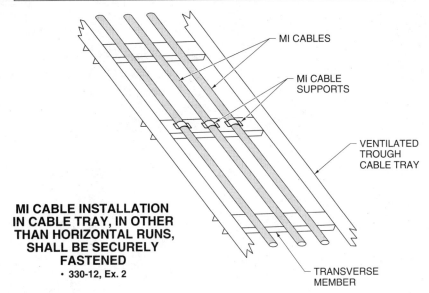

MI CABLES

MI CABLE SUPPORTS

VENTILATED TROUGH CABLE TRAY

MI CABLE INSTALLATION IN CABLE TRAY, IN OTHER THAN HORIZONTAL RUNS, SHALL BE SECURELY FASTENED
• 330-12, Ex. 2

TRANSVERSE MEMBER

MINERAL-INSULATED, METAL-SHEATHED CABLE

330-12, Ex. 2
NEW EXCEPTION

A new exception has been added to the requirements for support of MI cable. MI cable installed in cable trays shall comply with 318-8(b).

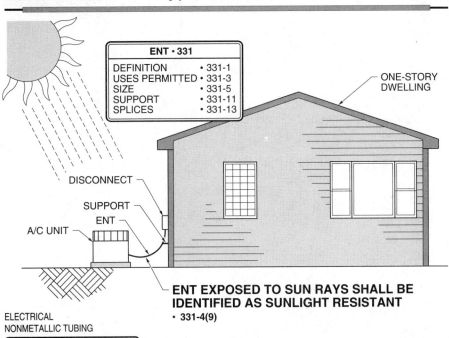

ENT • 331

DEFINITION	• 331-1
USES PERMITTED	• 331-3
SIZE	• 331-5
SUPPORT	• 331-11
SPLICES	• 331-13

ONE-STORY DWELLING

DISCONNECT

SUPPORT

ENT

A/C UNIT

ENT EXPOSED TO SUN RAYS SHALL BE IDENTIFIED AS SUNLIGHT RESISTANT
• 331-4(9)

ELECTRICAL NONMETALLIC TUBING

331-4(9)
NEW SUBSECTION

A new subpart requires that ENT installed where exposed to the rays of the sun, shall be identified as being sunlight resistant.

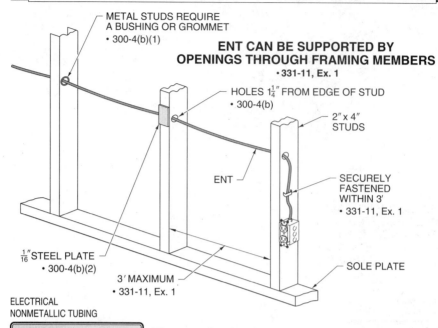

METAL STUDS REQUIRE
A BUSHING OR GROMMET
• 300-4(b)(1)

ENT CAN BE SUPPORTED BY
OPENINGS THROUGH FRAMING MEMBERS
• 331-11, Ex. 1

HOLES $1\frac{1}{4}''$ FROM EDGE OF STUD
• 300-4(b)

$2'' \times 4''$
STUDS

ENT

SECURELY
FASTENED
WITHIN 3'
• 331-11, Ex. 1

$\frac{1}{16}''$ STEEL PLATE
• 300-4(b)(2)

3' MAXIMUM
• 331-11, Ex. 1

SOLE PLATE

ELECTRICAL
NONMETALLIC TUBING

331-11, Ex. 1

REVISION

The exception has been revised to clarify support requirements for ENT. Openings through framing members can be used for support under specific conditions.

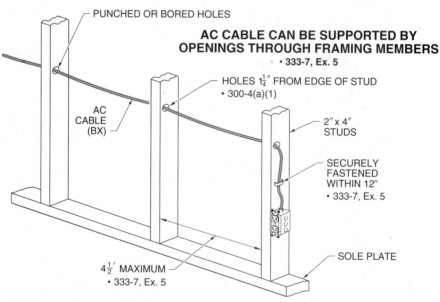

PUNCHED OR BORED HOLES

AC CABLE CAN BE SUPPORTED BY
OPENINGS THROUGH FRAMING MEMBERS
• 333-7, Ex. 5

HOLES $1\frac{1}{4}''$ FROM EDGE OF STUD
• 300-4(a)(1)

AC
CABLE
(BX)

$2'' \times 4''$
STUDS

SECURELY
FASTENED
WITHIN 12''
• 333-7, Ex. 5

$4\frac{1}{2}'$ MAXIMUM
• 333-7, Ex. 5

SOLE PLATE

ARMORED CABLE

333-7, Ex. 5

NEW EXCEPTION

A new exception will permit the use of punched or bored holes in framing members as the means of support for armored cable in other than vertical runs under specific conditions.

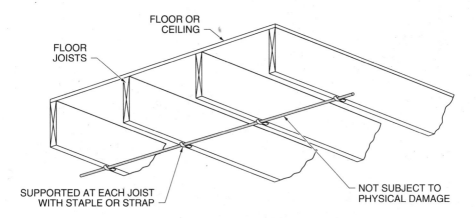

FLOOR OR CEILING

FLOOR JOISTS

SUPPORTED AT EACH JOIST WITH STAPLE OR STRAP

NOT SUBJECT TO PHYSICAL DAMAGE

**AC CABLE IS PERMITTED
TO RUN ON UNDERSIDE
OF JOISTS**
• 333-11

ARMORED CABLE

333-11

REVISION

Armored cable is now permitted to be run on the underside of joists in all locations, not just basements, if the cable is not subject to physical damage.

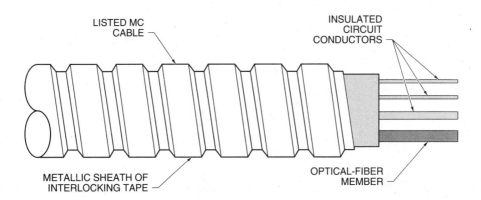

LISTED MC CABLE

INSULATED CIRCUIT CONDUCTORS

METALLIC SHEATH OF INTERLOCKING TAPE

OPTICAL-FIBER MEMBER

**MC CABLE CAN BE CONSTRUCTED
WITH OPTICAL-FIBER MEMBERS AND
INSULATED POWER CONDUCTORS**
• 334-1

METAL-CLAD CABLE

334-1

REVISION

The definition of metal-clad cable has been revised to include a listed metal-clad cable that contains optical-members along with the circuit conductors.

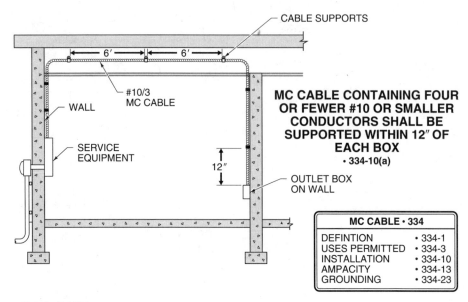

CABLE SUPPORTS

6'   6'

#10/3
MC CABLE

WALL

SERVICE
EQUIPMENT

12"

OUTLET BOX
ON WALL

**MC CABLE CONTAINING FOUR
OR FEWER #10 OR SMALLER
CONDUCTORS SHALL BE
SUPPORTED WITHIN 12" OF
EACH BOX**
• 334-10(a)

MC CABLE • 334	
DEFINTION	• 334-1
USES PERMITTED	• 334-3
INSTALLATION	• 334-10
AMPACITY	• 334-13
GROUNDING	• 334-23

METAL-CLAD CABLE

334-10(a)

REVISION

The support requirements for MC cable have been revised. The number and the size of the conductors determine whether the cable shall be supported within 12″ of a box, cabinet, or fitting.

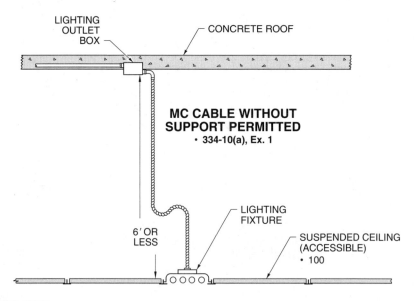

LIGHTING
OUTLET
BOX

CONCRETE ROOF

**MC CABLE WITHOUT
SUPPORT PERMITTED**
• 334-10(a), Ex. 1

LIGHTING
FIXTURE

6' OR
LESS

SUSPENDED CEILING
(ACCESSIBLE)
• 100

METAL-CLAD CABLE

334-10(a), Ex. 1

NEW EXCEPTION

A new exception has been added which permits MC cable to be installed from an outlet to a lighting fixture or equipment, without support, provided the total length is not more than 6′ and the installation is in an accessible ceiling.

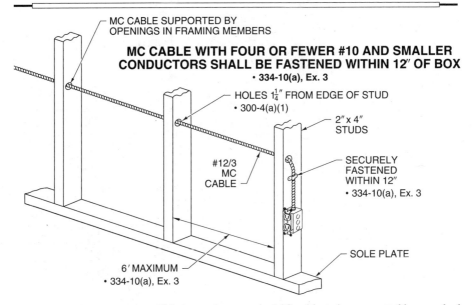

MC CABLE SUPPORTED BY
OPENINGS IN FRAMING MEMBERS

**MC CABLE WITH FOUR OR FEWER #10 AND SMALLER
CONDUCTORS SHALL BE FASTENED WITHIN 12″ OF BOX**
• 334-10(a), Ex. 3

HOLES $1\frac{1}{4}$″ FROM EDGE OF STUD
• 300-4(a)(1)

2″ x 4″
STUDS

#12/3
MC
CABLE

SECURELY
FASTENED
WITHIN 12″
• 334-10(a), Ex. 3

SOLE PLATE

6′ MAXIMUM
• 334-10(a), Ex. 3

METAL-CLAD CABLE

334-10(a), Ex. 3
NEW EXCEPTION

This exception permits MC cable to be supported by punched or bored holes through framing members provided the support intervals do not exceed 6′. In addition, cables containing four or fewer #10, and smaller, conductors shall be supported within 12″ of each outlet box, cabinet, fitting, etc.

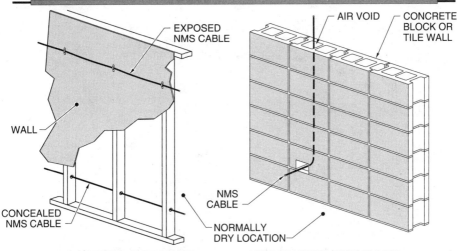

AIR VOID
CONCRETE
BLOCK OR
TILE WALL

EXPOSED
NMS CABLE

WALL

CONCEALED
NMS CABLE

NMS
CABLE

NORMALLY
DRY LOCATION

**NMS MAY BE INSTALLED
EXPOSED OR CONCEALED**
• 336-4(c)

**NMS MAY BE INSTALLED
OR FISHED**
• 336-4(c)

NONMETALLIC-SHEATHED CABLE

336
**REVISION AND
NEW SUBSECTION**

The entire Article has been rewritten. Part C now includes provisions for a new type of nonmetallic cable-sheathed cable (NMS). *NMS* is a factory assembled, nonmetallic-sheathed cable that consists of signaling, communications, and insulated power conductors within an overall outer jacket that is moisture-resistant and flame-retardant.

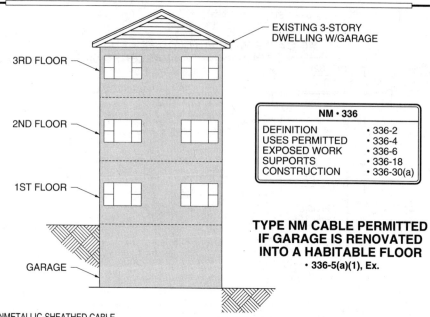

EXISTING 3-STORY
DWELLING W/GARAGE

3RD FLOOR

2ND FLOOR

1ST FLOOR

NM • 336	
DEFINITION	• 336-2
USES PERMITTED	• 336-4
EXPOSED WORK	• 336-6
SUPPORTS	• 336-18
CONSTRUCTION	• 336-30(a)

**TYPE NM CABLE PERMITTED
IF GARAGE IS RENOVATED
INTO A HABITABLE FLOOR**
• 336-5(a)(1), Ex.

GARAGE

NONMETALLIC-SHEATHED CABLE

336-5(a)(1), Ex.

NEW EXCEPTION

This exception permits NM cable to be used in buildings over three floors when a renovation to an existing one-family dwelling creates an additional habitable floor.

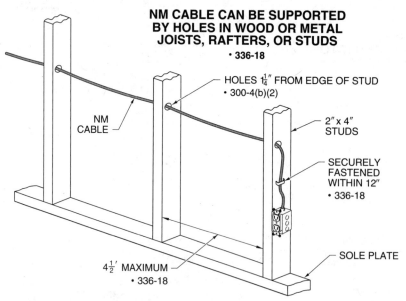

**NM CABLE CAN BE SUPPORTED
BY HOLES IN WOOD OR METAL
JOISTS, RAFTERS, OR STUDS**
• 336-18

HOLES $1\frac{1}{4}''$ FROM EDGE OF STUD
• 300-4(b)(2)

NM
CABLE

$2'' \times 4''$
STUDS

SECURELY
FASTENED
WITHIN 12''
• 336-18

SOLE PLATE

$4\frac{1}{2}'$ MAXIMUM
• 336-18

NONMETALLIC-SHEATHED CABLE

336-18

REVISION

This section has been revised to clarify that when NM cables are run through either bored or punched holes in metal or wood framing members, no additional supporting or securing is necessary.

FAHRENHEIT TO CELSIUS CONVERSION
$°C = \dfrac{(°F - 32)}{1.8}$

CELSIUS TO FAHRENHEIT CONVERSION
$°F = (1.8 \times °C) + 32$

DETERMINING NM CABLE AMPACITY

What is the final ampacity of #12/3 Romex in an ambient temperature of 105°F?

$$°C = \frac{(°F - 32)}{1.8} \qquad °C = \frac{105 - 32}{1.8} \qquad °C = \textbf{40.56}$$

336-30(b), Ex.: 90°C rating permitted
Table 310-16: 90°C = 30 A
Table 310-16, Correction Factors: 30 A x .87 = 26.1 A
336-30(b), Ex.: Final ampacity shall not exceed 60°C
Table 310-16: 60°C = 25 A
Final ampacity = **25 A**

NONMETALLIC-SHEATHED CABLE

336-30(b), Ex.
NEW EXCEPTION

When derating of NM cable is necessary, the derating shall be permitted from the 90°C rating, provided the final ampacity does not exceed that of the 60°C rating.

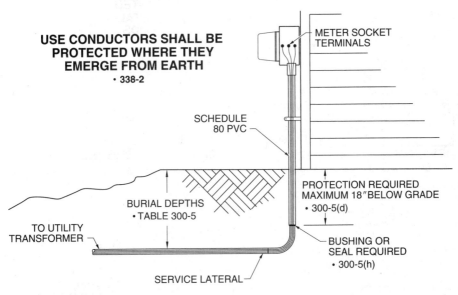

USE CONDUCTORS SHALL BE PROTECTED WHERE THEY EMERGE FROM EARTH
• 338-2

METER SOCKET TERMINALS

SCHEDULE 80 PVC

PROTECTION REQUIRED MAXIMUM 18″ BELOW GRADE
• 300-5(d)

BURIAL DEPTHS
• TABLE 300-5

TO UTILITY TRANSFORMER

BUSHING OR SEAL REQUIRED
• 300-5(h)

SERVICE LATERAL

SERVICE-ENTRANCE CABLE

338-2
REVISION

The uses permitted for SE cable have been revised to permit USE, used for service laterals, to emerge from the ground, if it is suitably protected per 300-5(d).

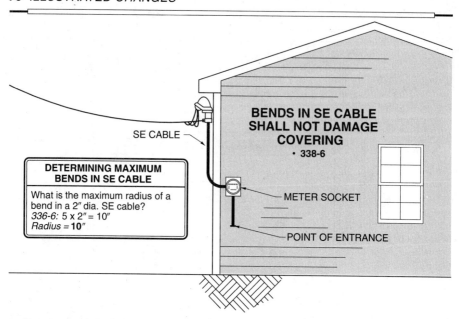

SE CABLE

BENDS IN SE CABLE SHALL NOT DAMAGE COVERING
• 338-6

DETERMINING MAXIMUM BENDS IN SE CABLE

What is the maximum radius of a bend in a 2″ dia. SE cable?
336-6: 5 x 2″ = 10″
Radius = **10″**

METER SOCKET

POINT OF ENTRANCE

SERVICE-ENTRANCE CABLE

338-6

NEW SECTION

New requirements for SE cable specify that bends in the cable be made so that the cables' outer covering is not damaged, and the radius of the inner edge of the cable is not less than 5 times the diameter of the cable.

UNDERGROUND FEEDER
AND BRANCH-CIRCUIT CABLE

339-1(a)

REVISION

The description of UF cable has been revised to require that only listed #14 through #4/0 Cu UF cables are permitted.

UNDERGROUND FEEDER
AND BRANCH-CIRCUIT CABLE

339-3(a)(2)

REVISION

The requirement that all single UF cables be installed in the same raceway or trench remains, but the term "subfeeder circuit" has been deleted from the NEC® because it is not defined.

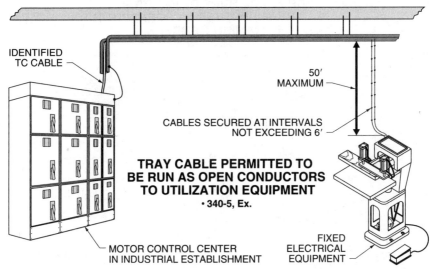

IDENTIFIED
TC CABLE

50'
MAXIMUM

CABLES SECURED AT INTERVALS
NOT EXCEEDING 6'

**TRAY CABLE PERMITTED TO
BE RUN AS OPEN CONDUCTORS
TO UTILIZATION EQUIPMENT**
• 340-5, Ex.

FIXED
ELECTRICAL
EQUIPMENT

MOTOR CONTROL CENTER
IN INDUSTRIAL ESTABLISHMENT

POWER AND
CONTROL TRAY CABLE

340-5, Ex.

NEW EXCEPTION

This exception permits TC cable, in industrial establishments only, where only qualified persons will service the installation, to be installed as open conductors in lengths not exceeding 50' from the cable tray system to the equipment. The cable shall be free from physical damage and supported at intervals not exceeding 6'.

NONMETALLIC UNDERGROUND
CONDUIT WITH CONDUCTORS

343-1

REVISION

The title of 343 has been changed from "Preassembled Cable in Nonmetallic Conduit" to "Nonmetallic Underground Conduit with Conductors." In addition, requirements for listing have been added.

NONMETALLIC UNDERGROUND
CONDUIT WITH CONDUCTORS

343-5(b)

REVISION

The maximum size permitted for nonmetallic underground conduit with conductors has been increased from 2″ to 4″.

HORIZONAL RUNS OF IMC OR RMC CAN BE SUPPORTED BY OPENINGS IN FRAMING MEMBERS
• 345-12, Ex. 4
• 346-12, Ex. 4

OPENINGS 1¼″ FROM EDGE OF STUD
• 300-4(a)(1)

2″ x 4″ STUDS

SECURELY FASTENED WITHIN 3′
• 345-12, Ex. 4

SOLE PLATE

STEEL PLATE NOT REQUIRED
• 300-4(a)(1), Ex.

10′ MAXIMUM
• 345-12, Ex. 4

INTERMEDIATE METAL CONDUIT

345-12, Ex. 4

NEW EXCEPTION

IMC, in horizontal runs, shall be permitted to be supported by the openings in framing members at intervals not exceeding 10′ and within 3′ of termination points. The same exception has been added to 346-12 for RMC.

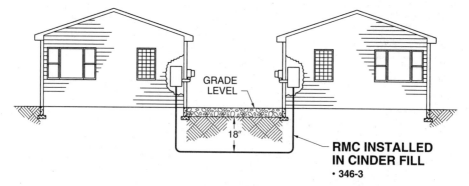

RMC INSTALLATION OPTIONS • 346-3
• PROTECT CONDUIT WITH 2″ OF NONCINDER CONCRETE
• LOCATE CONDUIT AT LEAST 18″ BELOW CINDER FILL
• PROTECT CONDUIT WITH CORROSION-RESISTANT MATERIAL

GRADE LEVEL

18″

RMC INSTALLED IN CINDER FILL
• 346-3

RIGID METAL CONDUIT

346-3

REVISION

The requirements for installing RMC in cinder fill have been modified. The three exceptions to the rule requiring that RMC not be installed in or under cinder fill subject to permanent moisture have been deleted. The provisions contained in the exceptions have been incorporated into the general rule.

RIGID NONMETALLIC CONDUIT

347-8, Ex.

NEW EXCEPTION

Openings through framing members shall be permitted to support horizontal runs of RNMC provided the intervals don't exceed those specified in Table 347-8, and the RNMC is supported within 3′ of termination points.

ELECTRICAL METALIC TUBING

348-12, Ex. 2

NEW EXCEPTION

This exception permits EMT to be installed without supports when it is used for concealed work in finished buildings or preassembled wall panels.

FLEXIBLE METAL CONDUIT • 350			
DEFINITION	• 350-2	CONDUCTORS	• 350-12
USES PERMITTED	• 350-4	GROUNDING	• 350-14
USES NOT PERMITTED	• 350-5	SUPPORTS	• 350-18
SIZE	• 350-10	SPLICES	• 350-24

FLEXIBLE METAL CONDUIT

350

REVISION

This article has been completely revised for clarity and to make it conform to the NEC® Style Manual. Grounding requirements have been revised to include, within the general rule, the requirement for installing an EGC anytime FMC is used where flexibility is required. See 350-14.

FLEXIBLE METAL CONDUIT

350-10(b)

NEW SUBSECTION

A new subsection has been added that limits the maximum size permitted for FMC to 4″ electrical trade size. The minimum size remains at $\frac{1}{2}$″ with five provisions for using $\frac{3}{8}$″ electrical trade size.

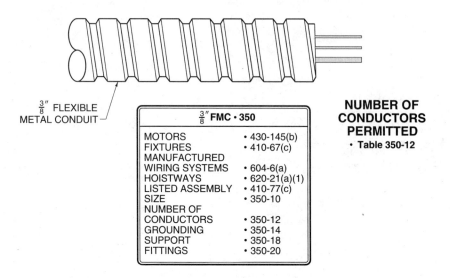

$\frac{3}{8}''$ FLEXIBLE
METAL CONDUIT

$\frac{3}{8}''$ FMC • 350	
MOTORS	• 430-145(b)
FIXTURES	• 410-67(c)
MANUFACTURED	
WIRING SYSTEMS	• 604-6(a)
HOISTWAYS	• 620-21(a)(1)
LISTED ASSEMBLY	• 410-77(c)
SIZE	• 350-10
NUMBER OF	
CONDUCTORS	• 350-12
GROUNDING	• 350-14
SUPPORT	• 350-18
FITTINGS	• 350-20

**NUMBER OF
CONDUCTORS
PERMITTED**
• **Table 350-12**

FLEXIBLE METAL CONDUIT

Table 350-12

REVISION

Table 350-12 lists the maximum number of insulated conductors that are permitted to be installed in $\frac{3}{8}''$ electrical trade size FMC. Many of the values in the Table have been adjusted downward, allowing fewer conductors in the conduit.

**LTFMC IS PERMITTED TO BE SUPPORTED
BY OPENINGS IN FRAMING MEMBERS**
• **351-8**

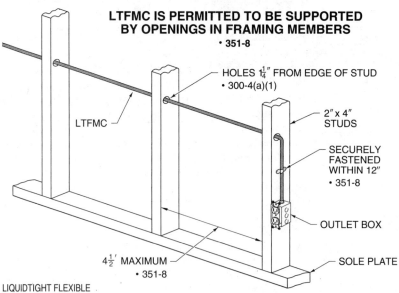

HOLES $1\frac{1}{4}''$ FROM EDGE OF STUD
• 300-4(a)(1)

LTFMC

2" x 4"
STUDS

SECURELY
FASTENED
WITHIN 12"
• 351-8

OUTLET BOX

$4\frac{1}{2}'$ MAXIMUM
• 351-8

SOLE PLATE

LIQUIDTIGHT FLEXIBLE
METAL CONDUIT AND LIQUIDTIGHT
FLEXIBLE NONMETALLIC CONDUIT

351-8

REVISION

Support requirements for LTFMC have been revised to permit the openings through framing members to provide the required support in horizontal runs. Support intervals shall not exceed $4\frac{1}{2}'$ and the conduit shall be fastened within 12" of boxes, enclosures, etc.

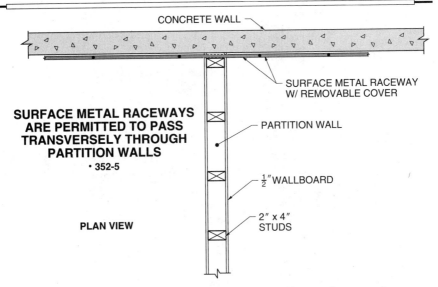

CONCRETE WALL

SURFACE METAL RACEWAY
W/ REMOVABLE COVER

PARTITION WALL

$\frac{1}{2}''$ WALLBOARD

$2'' \times 4''$
STUDS

**SURFACE METAL RACEWAYS
ARE PERMITTED TO PASS
TRANSVERSELY THROUGH
PARTITION WALLS**
• 352-5

PLAN VIEW

SURFACE METAL
RACEWAYS AND SURFACE
NONMETALLIC RACEWAYS

352-5

REVISION

The requirements for extending surface metal raceways through dry walls, partitions, and dry floors have been modified to require that raceways shall pass transversely through the wall, partition, etc., and the conductors shall be accessible on both sides of the wall, partition, or floor. The same text has been added to 352-28 for surface nonmetallic raceways.

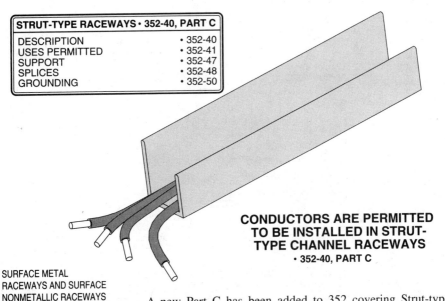

STRUT-TYPE RACEWAYS • 352-40, PART C	
DESCRIPTION	• 352-40
USES PERMITTED	• 352-41
SUPPORT	• 352-47
SPLICES	• 352-48
GROUNDING	• 352-50

**CONDUCTORS ARE PERMITTED
TO BE INSTALLED IN STRUT-
TYPE CHANNEL RACEWAYS**
• 352-40, PART C

SURFACE METAL
RACEWAYS AND SURFACE
NONMETALLIC RACEWAYS

352-40, Part C

NEW PART

A new Part C has been added to 352 covering Strut-type Channel Raceways. Some of the new sections provide requirements for permitted uses, number of conductors in raceways, support, grounding, and marking.

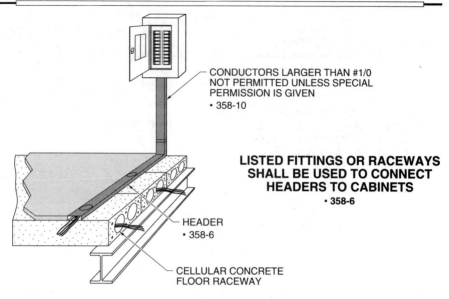

CONDUCTORS LARGER THAN #1/0
NOT PERMITTED UNLESS SPECIAL
PERMISSION IS GIVEN
• 358-10

**LISTED FITTINGS OR RACEWAYS
SHALL BE USED TO CONNECT
HEADERS TO CABINETS**
• 358-6

HEADER
• 358-6

CELLULAR CONCRETE
FLOOR RACEWAY

CELLULAR CONCRETE
FLOOR RACEWAYS

358-6

REVISION

This section has been revised to require that the connections made from the headers to all enclosures shall be made by means of listed metal raceways and fittings.

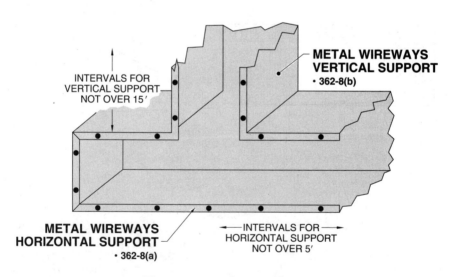

INTERVALS FOR
VERTICAL SUPPORT
NOT OVER 15'

**METAL WIREWAYS
VERTICAL SUPPORT**
• 362-8(b)

**METAL WIREWAYS
HORIZONTAL SUPPORT**
• 362-8(a)

◄—INTERVALS FOR—►
HORIZONTAL SUPPORT
NOT OVER 5'

METAL WIREWAYS AND
NONMETALLIC WIREWAYS

362-8

REVISION

The support requirements for metal wireways have been revised to incorporate the exception for vertical supports into the general rule. Subpart (a) lists the requirements for horizontal support and subpart (b) lists the requirements for vertical support. The same revision has been made to 362-22 for nonmetallic wireways.

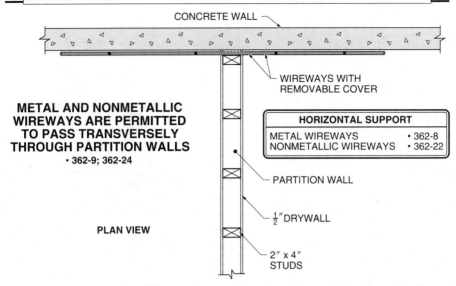

CONCRETE WALL

WIREWAYS WITH
REMOVABLE COVER

**METAL AND NONMETALLIC
WIREWAYS ARE PERMITTED
TO PASS TRANSVERSELY
THROUGH PARTITION WALLS**
• 362-9; 362-24

HORIZONTAL SUPPORT	
METAL WIREWAYS	• 362-8
NONMETALLIC WIREWAYS	• 362-22

PARTITION WALL

PLAN VIEW

$\frac{1}{2}''$DRYWALL

2″ x 4″
STUDS

METAL WIREWAYS AND
NONMETALLIC WIREWAYS

362-9

REVISION

The requirements for extending unbroken lengths of metal wireways have been revised to clarify that the wireway shall pass transversely through the wall, partition, or floor and the conductors shall be accessible on both sides of the wall, partition, or floor. The same revision has been made to 362-24 for nonmetallic wireway.

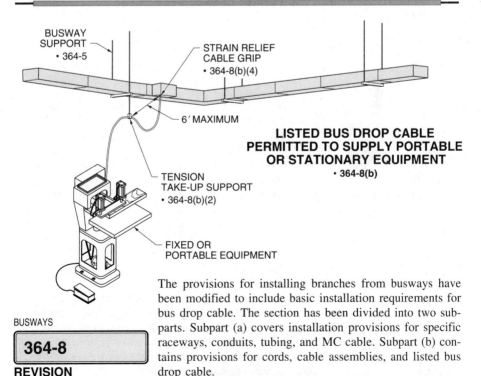

BUSWAY
SUPPORT
• 364-5

STRAIN RELIEF
CABLE GRIP
• 364-8(b)(4)

6′ MAXIMUM

**LISTED BUS DROP CABLE
PERMITTED TO SUPPLY PORTABLE
OR STATIONARY EQUIPMENT**
• 364-8(b)

TENSION
TAKE-UP SUPPORT
• 364-8(b)(2)

FIXED OR
PORTABLE EQUIPMENT

BUSWAYS

364-8

REVISION

The provisions for installing branches from busways have been modified to include basic installation requirements for bus drop cable. The section has been divided into two subparts. Subpart (a) covers installation provisions for specific raceways, conduits, tubing, and MC cable. Subpart (b) contains provisions for cords, cable assemblies, and listed bus drop cable.

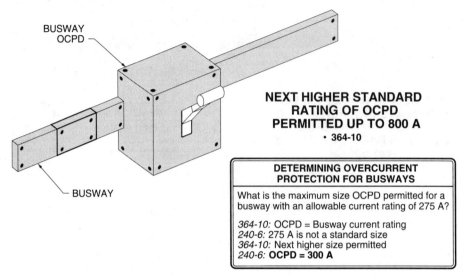

BUSWAY
OCPD

BUSWAY

**NEXT HIGHER STANDARD
RATING OF OCPD
PERMITTED UP TO 800 A**
• 364-10

**DETERMINING OVERCURRENT
PROTECTION FOR BUSWAYS**

What is the maximum size OCPD permitted for a
busway with an allowable current rating of 275 A?

364-10: OCPD = Busway current rating
240-6: 275 A is not a standard size
364-10: Next higher size permitted
240-6: **OCPD = 300 A**

BUSWAYS

364-10

REVISION

The provisions for determining the rating of the OCPD protecting busways have been modified to permit the use of the next higher standard rating if the allowable current rating of the busway does not correspond to a standard OCPD rating. Rounding-up is permitted only if the next higher rating does not exceed 800 A.

CABLEBUS

365-1

REVISION

The definition of cablebus has been revised. *Cablebus* is an assembly of insulated conductors installed in a completely enclosed, ventilated, metal enclosure. Cablebus is intended to be constructed in the field of components designed for the specific installation. Cablebus is designed to carry and withstand fault currents.

OUTLET, DEVICE,
PULL AND JUNCTION BOXES,
CONDUIT BODIES AND FITTINGS

370-1

REVISION

The term "conduit body" has replaced "fitting" where appropriate. The term "fitting" has been used incorrectly to refer to small conduit bodies. All references to "fitting" that deal with conduit bodies have been revised. In addition, a similar change has been made in 300-15 to specify conduit body instead of fitting.

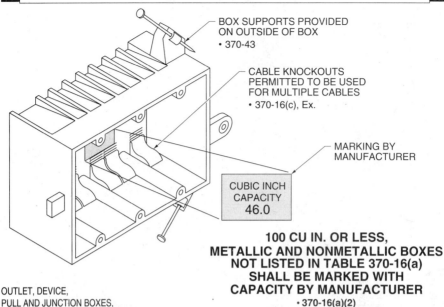

BOX SUPPORTS PROVIDED
ON OUTSIDE OF BOX
• 370-43

CABLE KNOCKOUTS
PERMITTED TO BE USED
FOR MULTIPLE CABLES
• 370-16(c), Ex.

MARKING BY
MANUFACTURER

CUBIC INCH
CAPACITY
46.0

**100 CU IN. OR LESS,
METALLIC AND NONMETALLIC BOXES
NOT LISTED IN TABLE 370-16(a)
SHALL BE MARKED WITH
CAPACITY BY MANUFACTURER**
• 370-16(a)(2)

OUTLET, DEVICE,
PULL AND JUNCTION BOXES,
CONDUIT BODIES AND FITTINGS

370-16(a)(2)

REVISION

The provisions for 100 cu in. or less boxes has been revised to clarify that nonmetallic as well as metallic boxes shall be legibly marked by the manufacturer with their cubic inch capacity.

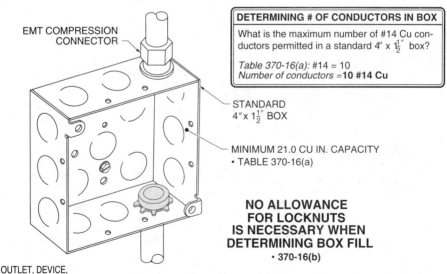

EMT COMPRESSION
CONNECTOR

DETERMINING # OF CONDUCTORS IN BOX

What is the maximum number of #14 Cu conductors permitted in a standard 4″ x 1½″ box?

Table 370-16(a): #14 = 10
*Number of conductors =***10 #14 Cu**

STANDARD
4″ x 1½″ BOX

MINIMUM 21.0 CU IN. CAPACITY
• TABLE 370-16(a)

**NO ALLOWANCE
FOR LOCKNUTS
IS NECESSARY WHEN
DETERMINING BOX FILL**
• 370-16(b)

OUTLET, DEVICE,
PULL AND JUNCTION BOXES,
CONDUIT BODIES AND FITTINGS

370-16(b)

REVISION

Box fill calculations have been revised to address each of the deductions separately. Small fittings, such as locknuts and bushings, do not need to be considered when calculating box fill.

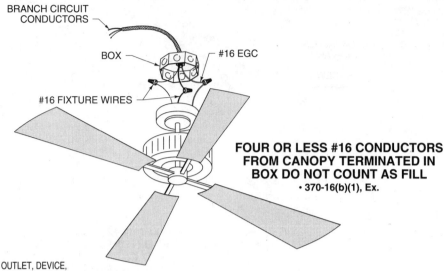

BRANCH CIRCUIT
CONDUCTORS

BOX

#16 EGC

#16 FIXTURE WIRES

**FOUR OR LESS #16 CONDUCTORS
FROM CANOPY TERMINATED IN
BOX DO NOT COUNT AS FILL**
• 370-16(b)(1), Ex.

OUTLET, DEVICE,
PULL AND JUNCTION BOXES,
CONDUIT BODIES AND FITTINGS

370-16(b)(1), Ex.
REVISION

The exception for conductor fill has been revised to specify that a fixture or similar domed canopy can provide space for not more than four #14 or smaller fixture wires and an EGC that terminates within the box.

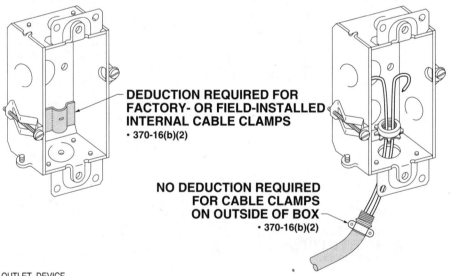

**DEDUCTION REQUIRED FOR
FACTORY- OR FIELD-INSTALLED
INTERNAL CABLE CLAMPS**
• 370-16(b)(2)

**NO DEDUCTION REQUIRED
FOR CABLE CLAMPS
ON OUTSIDE OF BOX**
• 370-16(b)(2)

OUTLET, DEVICE,
PULL AND JUNCTION BOXES,
CONDUIT BODIES AND FITTINGS

370-16(b)(2)
REVISION

The requirements for clamp fill deductions have been modified to clearly state that all internal cable clamps, whether field of factory installed, are to be considered when calculating box fill. No deduction for cable clamps on the outside of the box is necessary.

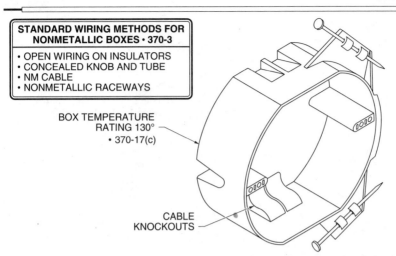

STANDARD WIRING METHODS FOR NONMETALLIC BOXES • 370-3
- OPEN WIRING ON INSULATORS
- CONCEALED KNOB AND TUBE
- NM CABLE
- NONMETALLIC RACEWAYS

BOX TEMPERATURE RATING 130°
• 370-17(c)

CABLE KNOCKOUTS

NONMETALLIC BOXES ARE PERMITTED TO BE INSTALLED IN CEILINGS AND WALLS
• 370-17(c), Ex.

OUTLET, DEVICE, PULL AND JUNCTION BOXES, CONDUIT BODIES AND FITTINGS

370-17(c), Ex.

REVISION

The first sentence of the exception has been modified to include ceilings, along with walls, as permissible locations for the use of nonmetallic boxes up to $2\frac{1}{4}'' \times 4''$. Nonmetallic boxes may be used to support smoke detectors and devices in ceilings as well as in walls.

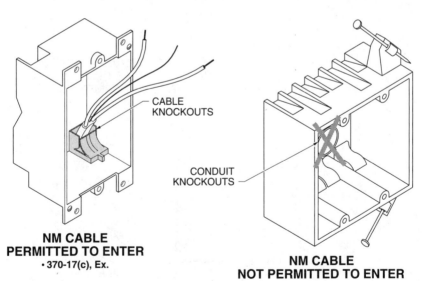

CABLE KNOCKOUTS

CONDUIT KNOCKOUTS

NM CABLE PERMITTED TO ENTER
• 370-17(c), Ex.

NM CABLE NOT PERMITTED TO ENTER
• 370-17(c), Ex.

OUTLET, DEVICE, PULL AND JUNCTION BOXES, CONDUIT BODIES AND FITTINGS

370-17(c), Ex.

REVISION

The exception has been revised to clarify that the only permissible entry point for nonmetallic-sheathed cables is through the cable knockouts. Knockouts designed for use with conduits are not permitted to be used for cable entry.

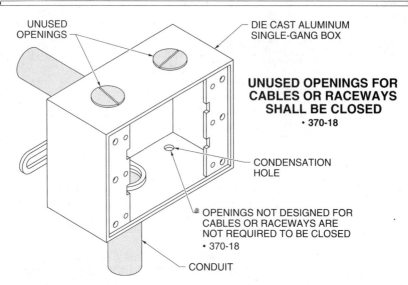

UNUSED OPENINGS

DIE CAST ALUMINUM
SINGLE-GANG BOX

**UNUSED OPENINGS FOR
CABLES OR RACEWAYS
SHALL BE CLOSED**
• 370-18

CONDENSATION
HOLE

OPENINGS NOT DESIGNED FOR
CABLES OR RACEWAYS ARE
NOT REQUIRED TO BE CLOSED
• 370-18

CONDUIT

OUTLET, DEVICE,
PULL AND JUNCTION BOXES,
CONDUIT BODIES AND FITTINGS

370-18

REVISION

The provision that unused openings in boxes, conduit bodies, and fittings be effectively sealed has been revised to specify only unused openings for cables and raceways shall be closed. This permits small holes, such as weep holes for condensation, to be made in boxes, conduit bodies, or fittings.

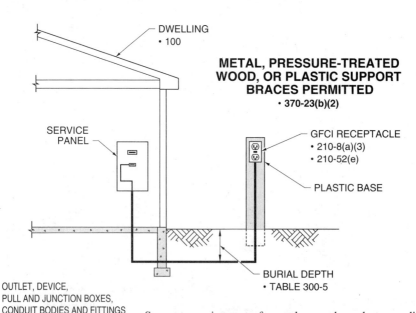

DWELLING
• 100

**METAL, PRESSURE-TREATED
WOOD, OR PLASTIC SUPPORT
BRACES PERMITTED**
• 370-23(b)(2)

SERVICE
PANEL

GFCI RECEPTACLE
• 210-8(a)(3)
• 210-52(e)

PLASTIC BASE

BURIAL DEPTH
• TABLE 300-5

OUTLET, DEVICE,
PULL AND JUNCTION BOXES,
CONDUIT BODIES AND FITTINGS

370-23(b)(2)

REVISION

Support requirements for enclosures have been modified to include polymeric braces as a permissible brace for enclosures supported directly from grade. Wood or polymeric braces used in wet locations shall be suitable for the conditions.

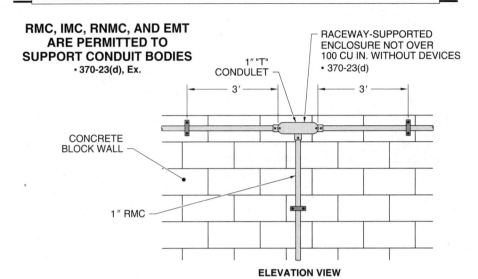

**RMC, IMC, RNMC, AND EMT
ARE PERMITTED TO
SUPPORT CONDUIT BODIES**
• 370-23(d), Ex.

RACEWAY-SUPPORTED
ENCLOSURE NOT OVER
100 CU IN. WITHOUT DEVICES
• 370-23(d)

1" "T"
CONDULET

CONCRETE
BLOCK WALL

1" RMC

ELEVATION VIEW

OUTLET, DEVICE,
PULL AND JUNCTION BOXES,
CONDUIT BODIES AND FITTINGS

370-23(d), Ex.

REVISION

The exception for raceway-supported enclosures without devices or fixtures has been revised to clarify that RMC, IMC, RNMC, or EMT is permitted to support conduit bodies, provided the conduit bodies do not exceed the size of the largest conduit or EMT.

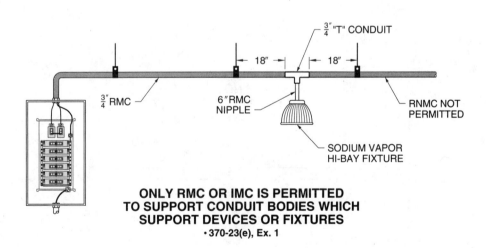

¾" "T" CONDUIT

18"   18"

¾" RMC

6" RMC
NIPPLE

RNMC NOT
PERMITTED

SODIUM VAPOR
HI-BAY FIXTURE

**ONLY RMC OR IMC IS PERMITTED
TO SUPPORT CONDUIT BODIES WHICH
SUPPORT DEVICES OR FIXTURES**
• 370-23(e), Ex. 1

OUTLET, DEVICE,
PULL AND JUNCTION BOXES,
CONDUIT BODIES AND FITTINGS

370-23(e), Ex. 1

REVISION

The exception for raceway-supported enclosures with devices or fixtures has been revised to clarify that only RMC or IMC is permitted to support conduit bodies, provided the conduit bodies do not exceed the size of the largest conduit or EMT. RNMC is not permitted to support equipment under this section.

OUTLET, DEVICE,
PULL AND JUNCTION BOXES,
CONDUIT BODIES AND FITTINGS

370-28, Ex.

REVISION

The exception following 370-28(a)(3) has been revised and relocated to 370-28. Relocating the exception ensures that the provisions for motor terminal housings apply to the entire section on pull and junction boxes.

OUTLET, DEVICE,
PULL AND JUNCTION BOXES,
CONDUIT BODIES AND FITTINGS

370-40(d)

REVISION

The requirements for grounding provisions in metal boxes have been revised. The provision that required a grounding means only when a metal box is used with nonmetallic raceways or cables has been deleted. The grounding means is permitted to be a tapped hole or the equivalent.

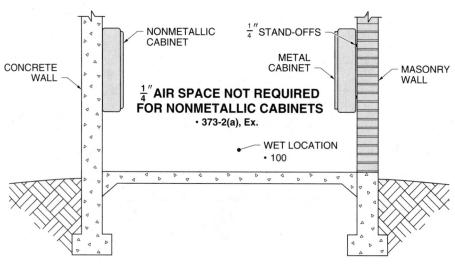

CABINETS,
CUTOUT BOXES, AND
METER SOCKET ENCLOSURES

373-2(a), Ex.

NEW EXCEPTION

The exception permits nonmetallic cabinets and cutout boxes to be installed without the ¼″ airspace between the enclosures and the wall or other surface used for support.

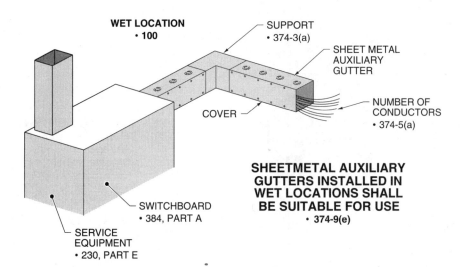

WET LOCATION
• **100**

SUPPORT
• 374-3(a)

SHEET METAL
AUXILIARY
GUTTER

NUMBER OF
CONDUCTORS
• 374-5(a)

COVER

SWITCHBOARD
• 384, PART A

SERVICE
EQUIPMENT
• 230, PART E

**SHEETMETAL AUXILIARY
GUTTERS INSTALLED IN
WET LOCATIONS SHALL
BE SUITABLE FOR USE**
• **374-9(e)**

AUXILIARY GUTTERS

374-9(e)

REVISION

The construction and installation requirements for auxiliary gutters in indoor and outdoor locations have been revised. Subpart (1) covers the installation of sheet metal auxiliary gutters in wet locations. Subpart (2) contains the requirements for nonmetallic auxiliary gutters installed outdoors.

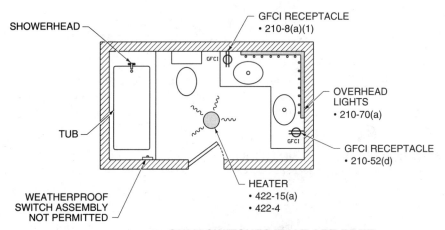

SHOWERHEAD

GFCI RECEPTACLE
• 210-8(a)(1)

OVERHEAD
LIGHTS
• 210-70(a)

TUB

GFCI RECEPTACLE
• 210-52(d)

WEATHERPROOF
SWITCH ASSEMBLY
NOT PERMITTED

HEATER
• 422-15(a)
• 422-4

**ONLY SWITCHES THAT ARE PART
OF LISTED ASSEMBLY ALLOWED**
• **380-4**

SWITCHES

380-4

REVISION

The last sentence of this section has been revised to clarify that switches cannot be installed in wet locations within the shower or tub area unless they are part of a listed tub or shower assembly.

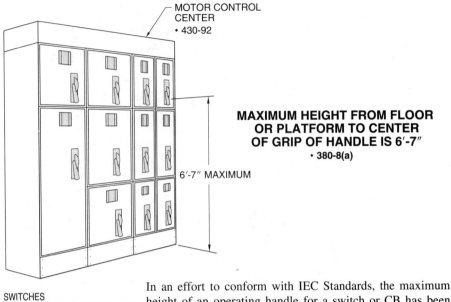

MOTOR CONTROL
CENTER
• 430-92

**MAXIMUM HEIGHT FROM FLOOR
OR PLATFORM TO CENTER
OF GRIP OF HANDLE IS 6′-7″**
• 380-8(a)

6′-7″ MAXIMUM

SWITCHES

380-8(a)

REVISION

In an effort to conform with IEC Standards, the maximum height of an operating handle for a switch or CB has been increased from 6′-6″ to 6′-7″. The measurement is determined from the floor or platform to the center of the grip of the handle.

SWITCHES

380-14(d)

NEW SUBSECTION

A new subsection has been added to the rating and use of snap switches. In an effort to harmonize the Canadian Electrical Code with the NEC®, listed snap switches rated 347 V AC are permitted for controlling noninductive and inductive loads not exceeding the ampere and voltage ratings of the switch.

SWITCHBOARDS
AND PANELBOARDS

384-4

REVISION

The installation requirements for switchboards and panelboards have been extensively revised. All four of the FPNs and three of the four exceptions have been deleted. Many of the provisions contained in these notes and exceptions have been incorporated into the general rule. Subpart (b) contains requirements for installations outdoors. Equipment installed outdoors shall be suitable for the conditions and shall be protected from spills, leaks, and accidental contact by unauthorized personnel.

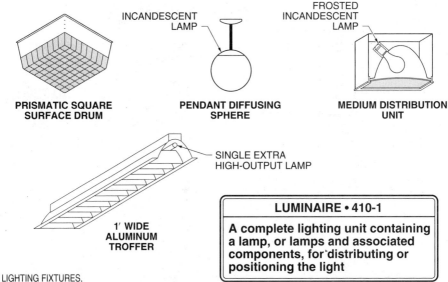

PRISMATIC SQUARE
SURFACE DRUM

INCANDESCENT
LAMP

PENDANT DIFFUSING
SPHERE

FROSTED
INCANDESCENT
LAMP

MEDIUM DISTRIBUTION
UNIT

SINGLE EXTRA
HIGH-OUTPUT LAMP

1' WIDE
ALUMINUM
TROFFER

LUMINAIRE • 410-1

A complete lighting unit containing a lamp, or lamps and associated components, for distributing or positioning the light

---

LIGHTING FIXTURES,
LAMPHOLDERS,
LAMPS, AND RECEPTACLES

410-1

NEW DEFINITION

The definition of luminaire has been added to 410. *Luminaire* is an international term which is used to designate a lighting fixture and the components used to distribute or position the light and connect it to a power source.

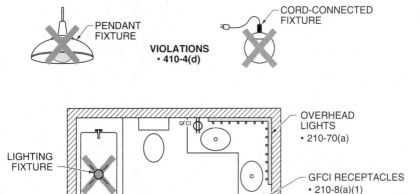

PENDANT
FIXTURE

CORD-CONNECTED
FIXTURE

**VIOLATIONS
• 410-4(d)**

LIGHTING
FIXTURE

TUB

OVERHEAD
LIGHTS
• 210-70(a)

GFCI RECEPTACLES
• 210-8(a)(1)
• 210-52(d)

**FIXTURES NOT PERMITTED
IN BATHTUB ZONE**
• 410-4(d)

LIGHTING FIXTURES,
LAMPHOLDERS,
LAMPS, AND RECEPTACLES

410-4(d)

REVISION

The title of the subsection has been changed from "Pendants" to "Above Bathtubs." This clarifies that all cord-connected fixtures are prohibited from being installed in the bathtub zone.

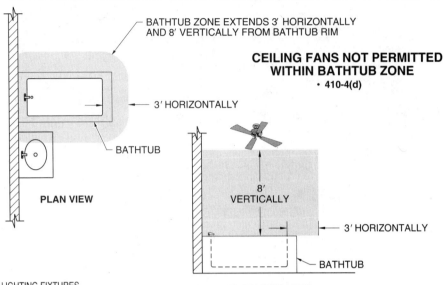

BATHTUB ZONE EXTENDS 3′ HORIZONTALLY
AND 8′ VERTICALLY FROM BATHTUB RIM

3′ HORIZONTALLY

BATHTUB

PLAN VIEW

CEILING FANS NOT PERMITTED WITHIN BATHTUB ZONE
• 410-4(d)

8′
VERTICALLY

3′ HORIZONTALLY

BATHTUB

ELEVATION VIEW

LIGHTING FIXTURES,
LAMPHOLDERS,
LAMPS, AND RECEPTACLES

410-4(d)

REVISION

Ceiling fans are not permitted to be installed above bathtubs in an area that extends from the rim of the top of the bathtub, 3′ horizontally and 8′ vertically. This zone includes the area directly above the bathtub.

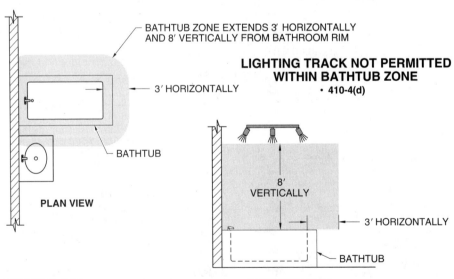

BATHTUB ZONE EXTENDS 3′ HORIZONTALLY
AND 8′ VERTICALLY FROM BATHROOM RIM

3′ HORIZONTALLY

BATHTUB

PLAN VIEW

LIGHTING TRACK NOT PERMITTED WITHIN BATHTUB ZONE
• 410-4(d)

8′
VERTICALLY

3′ HORIZONTALLY

BATHTUB

ELEVATION VIEW

LIGHTING FIXTURES,
LAMPHOLDERS,
LAMPS, AND RECEPTACLES

410-4(d)

REVISION

Lighting track has been added to the list of equipment that is not permitted to be installed in the zone around bathtubs that extends from the rim at the top of the bathtub, 3′ horizontally and 8′ vertically.

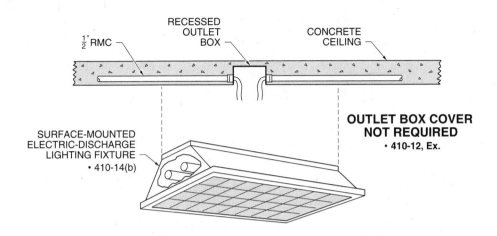

$\frac{1''}{2}$ RMC

RECESSED
OUTLET
BOX

CONCRETE
CEILING

**OUTLET BOX COVER
NOT REQUIRED**
• 410-12, Ex.

SURFACE-MOUNTED
ELECTRIC-DISCHARGE
LIGHTING FIXTURE
• 410-14(b)

LIGHTING FIXTURES,
LAMPHOLDERS,
LAMPS, AND RECEPTACLES

410-12, Ex.

NEW EXCEPTION

This exception permits outlet boxes to be installed without covers when surface-mounted electric-discharge lighting fixtures are installed over the outlet box.

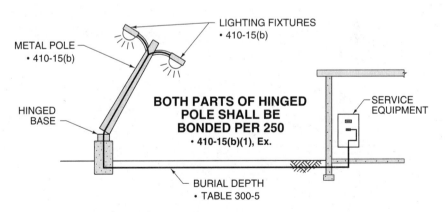

LIGHTING FIXTURES
• 410-15(b)

METAL POLE
• 410-15(b)

**BOTH PARTS OF HINGED
POLE SHALL BE
BONDED PER 250**
• 410-15(b)(1), Ex.

SERVICE
EQUIPMENT

HINGED
BASE

BURIAL DEPTH
• TABLE 300-5

LIGHTING FIXTURES,
LAMPHOLDERS,
LAMPS, AND RECEPTACLES

**410-15(b)(1),
Ex.**

REVISION

The provisions for bonding hinged-based lighting standards has been revised to specify that both parts of the hinged pole shall be bonded per 250.

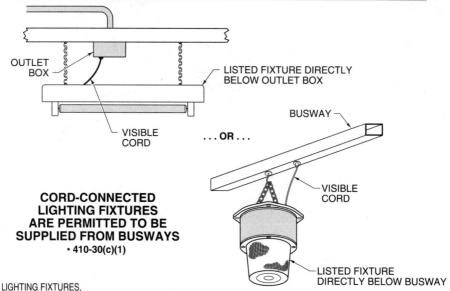

OUTLET BOX

LISTED FIXTURE DIRECTLY BELOW OUTLET BOX

VISIBLE CORD

... **OR** ...

BUSWAY

VISIBLE CORD

LISTED FIXTURE DIRECTLY BELOW BUSWAY

CORD-CONNECTED LIGHTING FIXTURES ARE PERMITTED TO BE SUPPLIED FROM BUSWAYS
• 410-30(c)(1)

LIGHTING FIXTURES, LAMPHOLDERS, LAMPS, AND RECEPTACLES

410-30(c)(1)
REVISION

Electric-discharge lighting is permitted to be cord-connected to busways provided the cord is continuously visible for its entire length and the fixture is located directly below the busway.

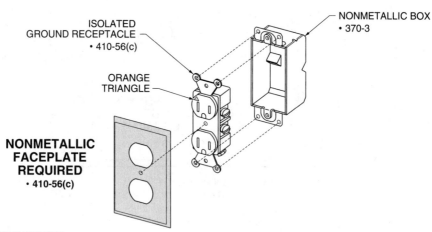

ISOLATED GROUND RECEPTACLE
• 410-56(c)

NONMETALLIC BOX
• 370-3

ORANGE TRIANGLE

NONMETALLIC FACEPLATE REQUIRED
• 410-56(c)

LIGHTING FIXTURES, LAMPHOLDERS, LAMPS, AND RECEPTACLES

410-56(c)
REVISION

The requirements for isolated ground (IG) receptacles have been modified so that when IG receptacles are installed in nonmetallic boxes they shall be covered with a nonmetallic faceplate.

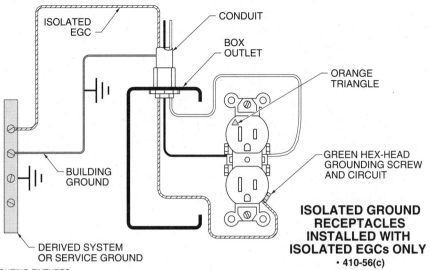

ISOLATED EGC

CONDUIT

BOX OUTLET

ORANGE TRIANGLE

GREEN HEX-HEAD GROUNDING SCREW AND CIRCUIT

BUILDING GROUND

DERIVED SYSTEM OR SERVICE GROUND

ISOLATED GROUND RECEPTACLES INSTALLED WITH ISOLATED EGCs ONLY
• 410-56(c)

LIGHTING FIXTURES, LAMPHOLDERS, LAMPS, AND RECEPTACLES

410-56(c)

REVISION

A new sentence has been added to the requirements for installing IG receptacles. IG receptacles, identified by an orange triangle on the receptacle face, are only permitted to be installed when an isolated equipment grounding conductor is provided.

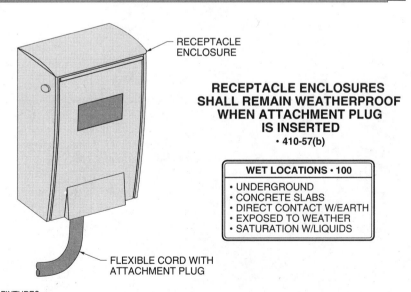

RECEPTACLE ENCLOSURE

RECEPTACLE ENCLOSURES SHALL REMAIN WEATHERPROOF WHEN ATTACHMENT PLUG IS INSERTED
• 410-57(b)

WET LOCATIONS • 100
• UNDERGROUND
• CONCRETE SLABS
• DIRECT CONTACT W/EARTH
• EXPOSED TO WEATHER
• SATURATION W/LIQUIDS

FLEXIBLE CORD WITH ATTACHMENT PLUG

LIGHTING FIXTURES, LAMPHOLDERS, LAMPS, AND RECEPTACLES

410-57(b)

REVISION

The section has been revised to clarify that when a receptacle is installed in a wet location, a weatherproof enclosure shall be provided. When attachment plugs are inserted, the integrity of the enclosure shall not be affected.

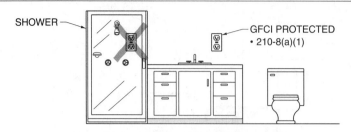

**RECEPTACLES ARE NOT PERMITTED TO BE
INSTALLED IN BATHTUB OR SHOWER SPACE**
• 410-57(c)

LIGHTING FIXTURES,
LAMPHOLDERS,
LAMPS, AND RECEPTACLES

410-57(c)
NEW SUBSECTION

A new subsection has been added to the requirements for receptacles in damp or wet locations. Receptacles are not permitted to be installed in a shower space or bathtub area.

LIGHTING FIXTURES,
LAMPHOLDERS,
LAMPS, AND RECEPTACLES

410-58(e)
REVISION

The requirements for grounding-type attachment plugs have been revised to clarify that the plugs shall only be used with cords equipped with an EGC. It was never the intent of this section to prohibit the use of grounding-type attachment plugs from being used in nongrounding receptacles with the appropriate adaptor.

LIGHTING FIXTURES,
LAMPHOLDERS,
LAMPS, AND RECEPTACLES

410-102
REVISION

The provisions for calculating lighting track loads have been revised. A calculated load of 150 VA, instead of 180 VA, is to be used for each 2' of track. A FPN has been added to clarify that it is not the intent of this section to limit the length of the track or the number of fixtures permitted.

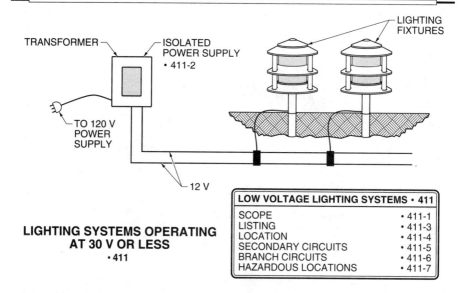

TRANSFORMER

ISOLATED
POWER SUPPLY
• 411-2

LIGHTING
FIXTURES

TO 120 V
POWER
SUPPLY

12 V

**LIGHTING SYSTEMS OPERATING
AT 30 V OR LESS**
• 411

LOW VOLTAGE LIGHTING SYSTEMS • 411	
SCOPE	• 411-1
LISTING	• 411-3
LOCATION	• 411-4
SECONDARY CIRCUITS	• 411-5
BRANCH CIRCUITS	• 411-6
HAZARDOUS LOCATIONS	• 411-7

LIGHTING SYSTEMS OPERATING
AT 30 VOLTS OR LESS

411

NEW ARTICLE

This new article covers low voltage lighting systems that consist of an isolating power supply operating at 30 V or less. Requirements for low voltage landscape lighting and low voltage interior lighting systems are contained in this article.

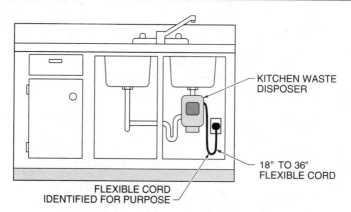

KITCHEN WASTE
DISPOSER

18″ TO 36″
FLEXIBLE CORD

FLEXIBLE CORD
IDENTIFIED FOR PURPOSE

**KITCHEN WASTE DISPOSERS CAN BE INSTALLED
IN ANY LOCATION IF ALL PROVISIONS ARE MET**
• 422-8(d)(1)

APPLIANCES

422-8(d)(1)

REVISION

The installation requirements for electrically-operated kitchen waste disposers now apply to occupancies other than just dwelling units. Kitchen waste disposers can be installed in any location, and can be cord-and plug-connected with flexible cord identified for the use. The length of the cord shall be not less than 18″ nor greater than 36″. The receptacle shall be accessible and located so that it will not subject the cord to physical damage.

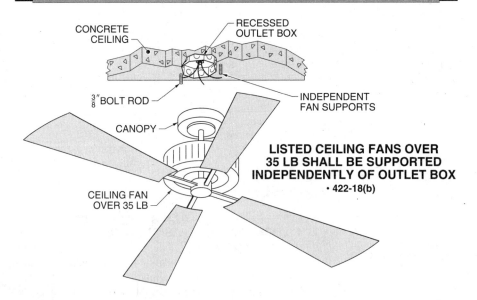

DISHWASHER PERMITTED TO BE CORD- AND PLUG-CONNECTED IF ALL PROVISIONS ARE MET
• 422-8(d)(2)

3′ TO 4′

FLEXIBLE CORD
• IDENTIFIED FOR PURPOSE
• NOT SUBJECT TO PHYSICAL DAMAGE

BUILT-IN DISHWASHER

APPLIANCES

422-8(d)(2)

REVISION

The installation requirements for built-in dishwashers and trash compactors now apply to occupancies other than just dwelling units. These appliances can be installed in any location and can be cord- and plug-connected with 3′ to 4′ lengths of flexible cord identified for the use. The receptacle shall be accessible, located in the space occupied by or adjacent to the appliance, and located so that it will not subject the cord to physical damage.

CONCRETE CEILING

RECESSED OUTLET BOX

$\frac{3}{8}$″ BOLT ROD

INDEPENDENT FAN SUPPORTS

CANOPY

LISTED CEILING FANS OVER 35 LB SHALL BE SUPPORTED INDEPENDENTLY OF OUTLET BOX
• 422-18(b)

CEILING FAN OVER 35 LB

APPLIANCES

422-18(a)(b)

REVISION

The provisions for support of ceiling fans has been revised by forming two subparts. Subpart (a) contains the requirements for supporting ceiling fans weighing 35 lb or less. Subpart (b) requires that ceiling fans weighing over 35 lb be supported independently of the box.

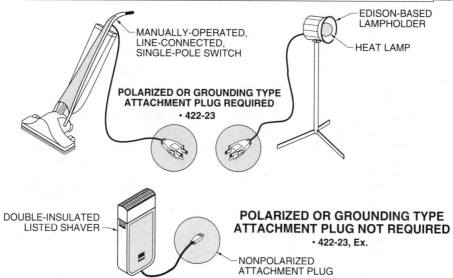

MANUALLY-OPERATED,
LINE-CONNECTED,
SINGLE-POLE SWITCH

EDISON-BASED
LAMPHOLDER

HEAT LAMP

**POLARIZED OR GROUNDING TYPE
ATTACHMENT PLUG REQUIRED**
• 422-23

DOUBLE-INSULATED
LISTED SHAVER

**POLARIZED OR GROUNDING TYPE
ATTACHMENT PLUG NOT REQUIRED**
• 422-23, Ex.

NONPOLARIZED
ATTACHMENT PLUG

APPLIANCES

422-23, Ex.

NEW EXCEPTION

The general rule of this section requires that appliances with a manually-operated, line-connected, single-pole switch or an Edison-base lampholder, or a 15 or 20 A receptacle be provided with a polarized or grounding-type attachment plug. The exception permits listed double-insulated shavers to be provided with a nonpolarized attachment plug.

FIXED ELECTRIC
SPACE-HEATING EQUIPMENT

424-19

REVISION

The requirements for the disconnecting means for fixed electric space-heating equipment have been revised to clarify that when fixed electric space-heating is supplied by more than one electrical source, the disconnecting means shall be grouped and marked.

FIXED ELECTRIC
SPACE-HEATING EQUIPMENT

424-35

REVISION

The permitted voltages for which electric space-heating cables can operate now include 480 V. The color code requirements for the lead wires have been revised to reflect the new voltage rating. The lead wire of cables operating at 480 V are colored orange.

FIXED ELECTRIC
SPACE-HEATING EQUIPMENT

424-44

REVISION

Electric space-heating cable requirements for installation in concrete or poured masonry have been revised. The $16\frac{1}{2}$ W/per linear foot limitation only applies to constant wattage heating cables. Self-regulating cables are not limited to a maximum wattage.

MOTORS, MOTOR CIRCUITS,
AND CONTROLLERS

430

REVISION

Requirements for sizing Design E, Branch-Circuit, Short-Circuit, and Ground-Fault Protective Devices have been added to Table 430-152. The FLC values for 3ϕ, AC motors in Table 430-150 have been revised to reflect the addition of Design E motors, which typically have higher FLCs.

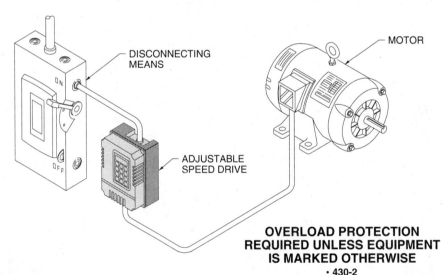

DISCONNECTING MEANS

MOTOR

ADJUSTABLE SPEED DRIVE

OVERLOAD PROTECTION REQUIRED UNLESS EQUIPMENT IS MARKED OTHERWISE
• 430-2

MOTORS, MOTOR CIRCUITS,
AND CONTROLLERS

430-2

REVISION

The requirements for adjustable speed drive systems have been modified to clarify that overload protection is required for power conversion equipment unless the equipment is marked otherwise.

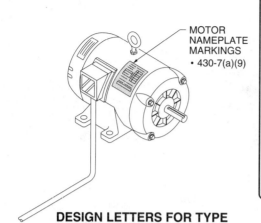

MOTOR
NAMEPLATE
MARKINGS
• 430-7(a)(9)

MOTOR NAMEPLATE DATA
• MANUFACTURERS' NAME
• VOLTAGE AND FLA
• FREQUENCY AND PHASE
• FULL LOAD SPEED
• TEMPERATURE RISE/ INSULATION CLASS
• TIME RATING
• HP
• CODE LETTER/LRA
• DESIGN LETTER
• SECONDARY VOLTS AND FLA FOR WOUND-ROTOR MOTORS
• FIELD CURRENT AND VOLTAGE FOR DC SYNCHRONOUS MOTORS
• WINDING TYPE FOR DC MOTORS
• THERMAL PROTECTION
• IMPEDANCE PROTECTION

**DESIGN LETTERS FOR TYPE
B, C, D, OR E MOTORS SHALL
BE INCLUDED ON NAMEPLATE**
• 430-7(a)(9)

MOTORS, MOTOR CIRCUITS,
AND CONTROLLERS

430-7(a)(9)

NEW FPN

The list of information that shall be marked on a motor has been expanded to include the design letter. An FPN has been added to reference available sources for design letter definitions.

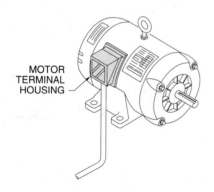

MOTOR
TERMINAL
HOUSING

WIRE SPACE COMPARISONS		
HP	USABLE VOLUME*	
	1993 NEC®	1996 NEC®
1 AND LESS	7.5	10.5
$1\frac{1}{2}$, 2, 3	12	16.8
5, $7\frac{1}{2}$	16	22.4
10, 15	26	36.4

* in cu in.

**MOTOR TERMINAL HOUSINGS
HAVE BEEN INCREASED
APPROXIMATELY 40%
FOR WIRE TERMINATIONS**
• TABLE 430-12(b)

MOTORS, MOTOR CIRCUITS,
AND CONTROLLERS

Table 430-12(b)

REVISION

The dimensions for wire-to-wire connections in motor terminal housings have been increased by 40% to provide more space for the connections. This makes terminations easier in cases where the wire size is increased, such as for voltage drop.

FULL VOLTAGE
MOTOR STARTER

**OVERLOAD PROTECTION
IS SIZED FROM MOTOR
NAMEPLATE FLC, NOT
TABLE CURRENTS**
• 430-34

MOTORS WITH MARKED SF
OF NOT LESS THAN 1.15
PERMITTED TO BE SIZED AT
140% WHEN STARTING
CURRENT IS A PROBLEM
• 430-34

MOTORS, MOTOR CIRCUITS,
AND CONTROLLERS

430-34

REVISION

The calculation for the selection of overload relays when the overloads are not sufficient to start the motor or carry the load has been revised. The increased values permitted by this section are based on the motor nameplate full-load current rating.

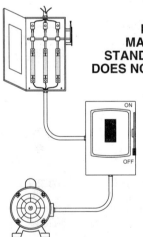

**MBCSCGF PROTECTIVE DEVICES
MAY BE INCREASED TO NEXT HIGHER
STANDARD SIZE WHEN CALCULATED VALUE
DOES NOT CORRESPOND TO STANDARD RATING**
• 430-52(c)(1), Ex. 1

DETERMINING MBCSCGF PROTECTIVE DEVICES

What size MBCSCGF protective device is required for a 20 HP, 230 V, 3ϕ induction motor using NTDFs?

Table 430-150: 20 HP = 54 A
Table 430-152: 54 A x 300% = 162 A
240-6: 162 A is not standard size
430-52(C)(1), Ex. 1: Next higher size = 175 A
NTDFs = **175 A**

MOTORS, MOTOR CIRCUITS,
AND CONTROLLERS

430-52(c)(1), Ex. 1

REVISION

"Rounding up" is permitted when selecting MBCSCGF devices which do not correspond to a standard rating of an OCPD.

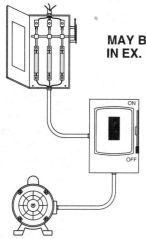

**MBCSCGF PROTECTIVE DEVICE
MAY BE INCREASED IF RATING CALCULATED
IN EX. 1 DOES NOT PERMIT MOTOR TO START**
• 430-52(c)(1), Ex. 2

DETERMINING MAXIMUM MBCSCGF PROTECTIVE DEVICES

What is the maximum size MBCSCGF protective device permitted for a 20 HP, 230 V, 3φ induction motor using NTDFs when rating per 430-52(C)(1), Ex. 1 is not sufficent?

Table 430-150: 20 HP = 54 A
430-52(c)(1), Ex. 2: 54 A x 400% = 216 A
240-6: 216 A is not standard size
NTDFs = **200 A**

MOTORS, MOTOR CIRCUITS,
AND CONTROLLERS

430-52(c)(1), Ex. 2
REVISION

Ex. 2 has been revised to clarify that it is to be used only when the ratings obtained in Ex. 1, after "rounding up," do not permit the motor to start.

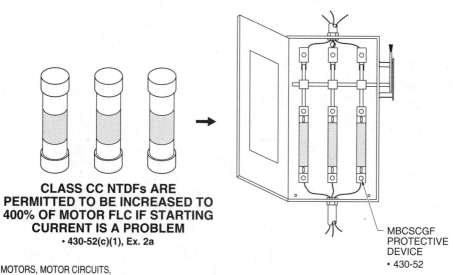

**CLASS CC NTDFs ARE
PERMITTED TO BE INCREASED TO
400% OF MOTOR FLC IF STARTING
CURRENT IS A PROBLEM**
• 430-52(c)(1), Ex. 2a

MBCSCGF
PROTECTIVE
DEVICE
• 430-52

MOTORS, MOTOR CIRCUITS,
AND CONTROLLERS

430-52(c)(1), Ex. 2a
REVISION

Subpart a has been expanded to permit Class CC TDFs to be increased to a maximum of 400% of the full-load current when the OCPD or thermal device selected in Ex.1 does not permit the motor to start.

MOTORS, MOTOR CIRCUITS,
AND CONTROLLERS

430-52(c)(3)

REVISION

Instantaneous trip CBs (ITBs) are permitted only if they are adjustable and are part of a listed combination motor controller. The motor controller shall have full overcurrent protection in each phase and the setting shall be based on the values listed in Table 430-152.

MOTORS, MOTOR CIRCUITS,
AND CONTROLLERS

**430-52(c)(3),
Ex. 1**

REVISION

The exception, which permits an increased setting for ITBs when the Table values listed in 430-152 do not permit the motor to start, has been revised. For Design E motors, the setting may be increased up to a maximum of 1700% of the FLC. However, trip settings over 1100% for Design E motors and 800% for other than Design E motors are permitted only after the need is demonstrated and an engineering evaluation has been performed.

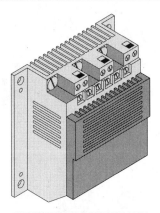
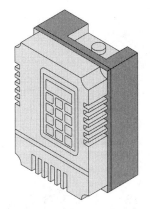

SOLID-STATE CONTROLLER   **ADJUSTABLE SPEED DRIVE SYSTEM**

**POWER ELECTRONIC DEVICES
PERMITTED TO BE PROTECTED
BY SUITABLE FUSES**
• 430-52(c)(5)

MOTORS, MOTOR CIRCUITS,
AND CONTROLLERS

430-52(c)(5)

REVISION

The term "adjustable speed drive system" has been replaced with "power electronic devices." This clarifies that the permission to use suitable fuses in lieu of the devices listed in Table 430-52 applies to solid-state motor controllers as well as AC drives.

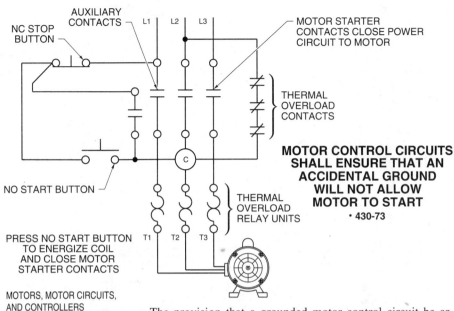

AUXILIARY CONTACTS

NC STOP BUTTON

L1 L2 L3

MOTOR STARTER CONTACTS CLOSE POWER CIRCUIT TO MOTOR

THERMAL OVERLOAD CONTACTS

NO START BUTTON

C

MOTOR CONTROL CIRCUITS SHALL ENSURE THAT AN ACCIDENTAL GROUND WILL NOT ALLOW MOTOR TO START
• **430-73**

THERMAL OVERLOAD RELAY UNITS

PRESS NO START BUTTON TO ENERGIZE COIL AND CLOSE MOTOR STARTER CONTACTS

T1 T2 T3

MOTORS, MOTOR CIRCUITS, AND CONTROLLERS

430-73

REVISION

The provision that a grounded motor control circuit be arranged so that an accidental ground will not start the motor or bypass safety devices has been revised to specify that the requirement applies to the entire control circuit.

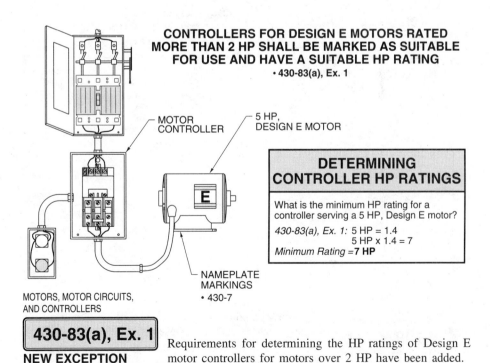

CONTROLLERS FOR DESIGN E MOTORS RATED MORE THAN 2 HP SHALL BE MARKED AS SUITABLE FOR USE AND HAVE A SUITABLE HP RATING
• **430-83(a), Ex. 1**

MOTOR CONTROLLER

5 HP, DESIGN E MOTOR

E

DETERMINING CONTROLLER HP RATINGS

What is the minimum HP rating for a controller serving a 5 HP, Design E motor?

430-83(a), Ex. 1: 5 HP = 1.4
5 HP x 1.4 = 7
*Minimum Rating =***7 HP**

NAMEPLATE MARKINGS
• 430-7

MOTORS, MOTOR CIRCUITS, AND CONTROLLERS

430-83(a), Ex. 1

NEW EXCEPTION

Requirements for determining the HP ratings of Design E motor controllers for motors over 2 HP have been added.

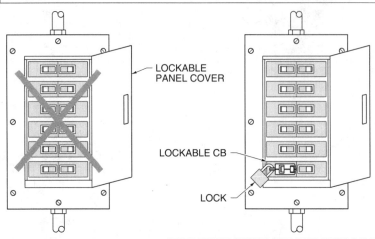

**CBs BEHIND LOCKED
PANEL COVER NOT PERMITTED
AS DISCONNECTING MEANS**
• 430-102(b), Ex.

**DISCONNECTING MEANS NOT LOCATED IN
SIGHT OF MOTOR SHALL BE CAPABLE
OF BEING INDIVIDUALLY LOCKED OPEN**
• 430-102(b), Ex.

MOTORS, MOTOR CIRCUITS,
AND CONTROLLERS

430-102(b), Ex.
REVISION

Disconnecting means which are not in sight of the motor shall be capable of being individually locked in the open position.

**MOTOR-CIRCUIT SWITCH
PERMITTED AS DISCONNECTING
MEANS IF RATED FOR USE WITH
DESIGN E MOTORS AND SIZED
WITH SUITABLE HP RATING**
• 430-109, Ex. 1

DETERMINING MOTOR-CIRCUIT SWITCH HP RATINGS

What is the minimum HP rating for a motor-circuit switch serving a 5 HP, Design E motor?

430-109, Ex. 1: 5 HP = 1.4
5 HP x 1.4 = 7
Minimum Rating = **7 HP**

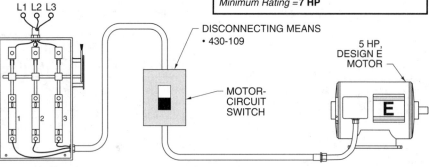

MOTORS, MOTOR CIRCUITS,
AND CONTROLLERS

430-109, Ex. 1
NEW EXCEPTION

This new exception has been added to the requirements for motor-switches used with Design E motors. The switches are required to be marked for use with Design E motors and shall have the appropriate HP rating.

MOTORS, MOTOR CIRCUITS,
AND CONTROLLERS

Table 430-150

REVISION

The table values for 3φ, AC motors have been increased. The values for motors under 2 HP have, in many cases, been found to be too low. In addition, FLC values have been added for motors from 250 HP through 500 HP.

MOTORS, MOTOR CIRCUITS,
AND CONTROLLERS

Table 430-152

REVISION

Table 430-152 has been completely revised and simplified. References to motor code letters and most motor types have been largely deleted. Motor design types have been added, and the column for NTDFs has been expanded to include Class CC fuses.

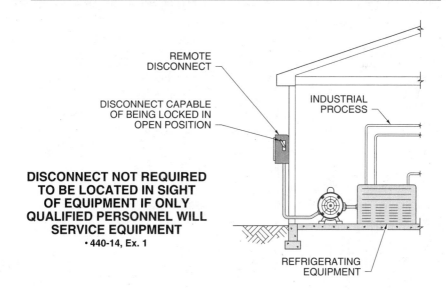

REMOTE
DISCONNECT

DISCONNECT CAPABLE
OF BEING LOCKED IN
OPEN POSITION

INDUSTRIAL
PROCESS

**DISCONNECT NOT REQUIRED
TO BE LOCATED IN SIGHT
OF EQUIPMENT IF ONLY
QUALIFIED PERSONNEL WILL
SERVICE EQUIPMENT**
• 440-14, Ex. 1

REFRIGERATING
EQUIPMENT

AIR-CONDITIONING AND
REFRIGERATING EQUIPMENT

440-14, Ex. 1

NEW EXCEPTION

The requirements for location of the disconnecting means for motor compressors and A/C equipment have been revised. If the equipment is part of an industrial process, a disconnect need not be installed within sight of the equipment when all conditions of the exception are met.

NEUTRAL CONDUCTORS SHALL BE SIZED AT LEAST AS LARGE AS MINIMUM REQUIRED SIZE OF LARGEST PHASE CONDUCTOR
• 445-5, Ex. 3

GENERATORS • 445	
LOCATION	• 445-2
OVERCURRENT PROTECTION	• 445-4
AMPACITY	• 445-5
PROTECTION	• 445-6
BUSHINGS	• 445-8

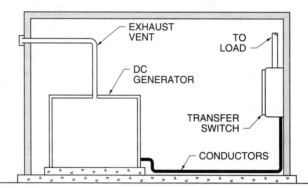

GENERATORS

445-5, Ex. 3

NEW EXCEPTION

This new exception requires that neutral conductors of DC generators shall be sized at least the same as the largest phase conductor if they are required to carry ground-fault currents.

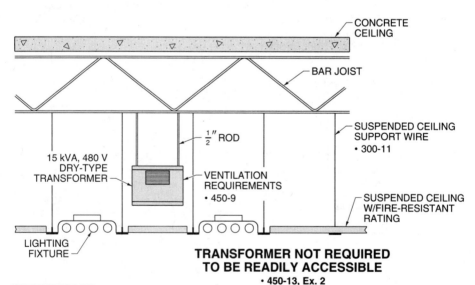

TRANSFORMER NOT REQUIRED TO BE READILY ACCESSIBLE
• 450-13, Ex. 2

TRANSFORMERS AND TRANSFORMER VAULTS

450-13, Ex. 2

REVISION

The requirements for the location of dry-type transformers rated 600 V or less have been revised to clarify that transformers located in fire-resistant spaces of buildings need not be readily accessible.

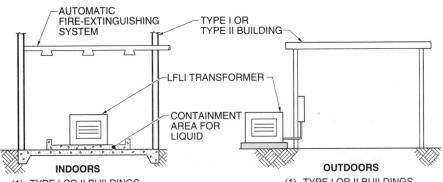

INDOORS

(1) TYPE I OR II BUILDINGS
  • RATED 35,000 V OR LESS
  • NO COMBUSTIBLE MATERIALS
  • LIQUID CONFINEMENT AREA
  • LISTING REQUIREMENTS

(2) AUTOMATIC FIRE-
  EXTINGUISHING SYSTEM

(3) PER 450-26

OUTDOORS

(1) TYPE I OR II BUILDINGS
  • AS PER LIQUID
    LISTING REQUIREMENTS

(2) PER 450-27

**LFLI TRANSFORMER
INSTALLATIONS**
• 450-23(a)(b)

TRANSFORMERS AND
TRANSFORMER VAULTS

450-23(a)(b)

REVISION

The section covering the installation requirements for less-flammable, liquid-insulated (LFLI) transformers has been completely revised. Subpart (a) contains the requirements for indoor installations and subpart (b) contains the provisions for LFLI transformers installed outdoors.

**MANUFACTURED PHASE IS NOT
SOLIDLY CONNECTED TO
EITHER INPUT CONDUCTOR**
• 455-2

PHASE CONVERTERS • 455	
AMPACITY	• 455-6
OVERCURRENT PROTECTION	• 455-7
DISCONNECTING MEANS	• 455-8
CONNECTION	• 455-9
TERMINAL HOUSINGS	• 455-10

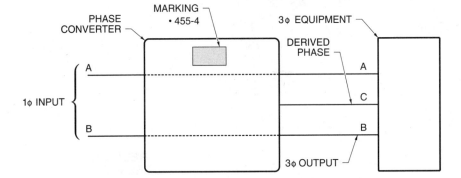

PHASE CONVERTERS

455-2

NEW DEFINITION

The term "manufactured phase" has been added to the definitions in this section. The *manufactured phase* is the derived phase that has no electrical connection to the single-phase input at the phase converter.

PHASE CONVERTERS

455-2
NEW DEFINITION

The term rotary phase converter has been added to the definitions in this section. A *rotary phase conductor* is constructed with a rotary transformer and capacitor panel(s) and allows a 3ϕ load to operate from a 1ϕ supply.

PHASE CONVERTERS

455-2
NEW DEFINITION

The term static phase converter has been added to the definitions in this section. A *static phase converter* converts a 1ϕ input to a 3ϕ output without any rotating parts.

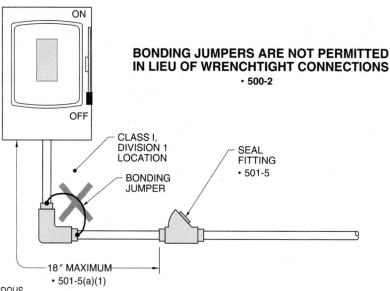

BONDING JUMPERS ARE NOT PERMITTED IN LIEU OF WRENCHTIGHT CONNECTIONS
• 500-2

ON

OFF

CLASS I,
DIVISION 1
LOCATION

BONDING
JUMPER

SEAL
FITTING
• 501-5

18″ MAXIMUM
• 501-5(a)(1)

HAZARDOUS
(CLASSIFIED) LOCATIONS

500-2
REVISION

The purpose of wrenchtight connections is to prevent, not minimize, sparking under fault conditions. The permission to use bonding jumpers around a threaded joint in conduit systems installed in hazardous locations has been deleted.

HAZARDOUS LOCATIONS

STANDARD SYSTEM	OPTIONAL SYSTEM
500; 501; 502; 503	500; 501; 502; 503; 505

CLASS I	FLAMMABLE GASES OR VAPORS
DIVISION 1	NORMALLY PRESENT IN AIR
DIVISION 2	NOT NORMALLY PRESENT IN AIR
CLASS II	COMBUSTIBLE DUST
DIVISION 1	NORMALLY PRESENT IN AIR
DIVISION 2	NOT NORMALLY PRESENT IN AIR
CLASS III	IGNITIBLE FIBERS OR FLYINGS
DIVISION 1	NORMALLY PRESENT IN AIR
DIVISION 2	NOT NORMALLY PRESENT IN AIR

ZONE 0	FLAMMABLE GASES OR VAPORS ARE PRESENT CONTINUOUSLY OR FOR LONG PERIODS OF TIME
ZONE 1	FLAMMABLE GASES OR VAPORS ARE LIKELY TO EXIST UNDER NORMAL OPERATING CONDITIONS OR EXIST FREQUENTLY
ZONE 2	FLAMMABLE GASES OR VAPORS ARE NOT NORMALLY PRESENT OR ARE PRESENT FOR SHORT PERIODS OF TIME

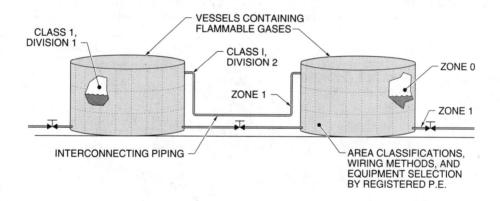

CLASS 1, DIVISION 1

VESSELS CONTAINING FLAMMABLE GASES

CLASS I, DIVISION 2

ZONE 1

ZONE 0

ZONE 1

INTERCONNECTING PIPING

AREA CLASSIFICATIONS, WIRING METHODS, AND EQUIPMENT SELECTION BY REGISTERED P.E.

OPTIONAL CLASSIFICATION SYSTEM CAN ONLY BE USED UNDER SUPERVISION OF A QUALIFIED REGISTERED PROFESSIONAL ENGINEER
· 500-3

HAZARDOUS
(CLASSIFIED) LOCATIONS

500-3

REVISION

A new, optional system for classifying hazardous locations will not replace the existing classification system, but will introduce an alternative method. Essentially, in an effort to harmonize international standards, a new 505, Zone 0, 1, and 2 locations have been added.

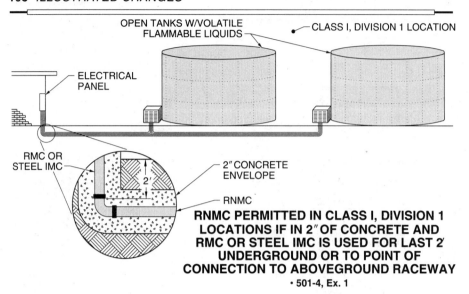

OPEN TANKS W/VOLATILE FLAMMABLE LIQUIDS

CLASS I, DIVISION 1 LOCATION

ELECTRICAL PANEL

RMC OR STEEL IMC

2″ CONCRETE ENVELOPE

2′

RNMC

RNMC PERMITTED IN CLASS I, DIVISION 1 LOCATIONS IF IN 2″ OF CONCRETE AND RMC OR STEEL IMC IS USED FOR LAST 2′ UNDERGROUND OR TO POINT OF CONNECTION TO ABOVEGROUND RACEWAY
• 501-4, Ex. 1

CLASS I LOCATIONS

501-4, Ex.1

NEW EXCEPTION

RNMC is permitted to be used as a wiring method in Class I, Division 1 locations provided it is encased in concrete at least 2″ thick and buried at a depth of at least 2′. RMC or IMC shall be used for the last 2′ underground, and to the point of connection or emergence of the aboveground raceway.

MC CABLE PERMITTED IN CLASS I, DIVISION 1 LOCATIONS
• 501-4, Ex. 2

MC PERMITTED — CLASS I, DIVISION 1
• **INDUSTRIAL PREMISES**
• **LIMITED PUBLIC ACCESS**
• **QUALIFIED PERSONNEL**
• **LISTED**
• **GAS/VAPORTIGHT, AL SHEATH**
• **OUTER POLYMERIC JACKET**

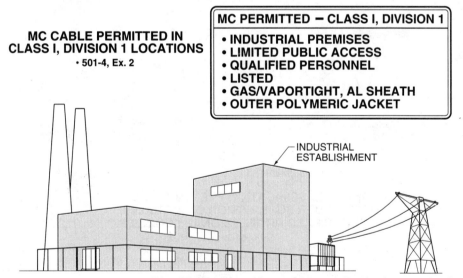

INDUSTRIAL ESTABLISHMENT

CLASS I LOCATIONS

501-4, Ex. 2

NEW EXCEPTION

Listed MC cable with a gas/vaportight, continuous, aluminum sheath and an outer jacket of a suitable polymeric material is permitted to be installed in a Class I, Division 1 location provided it is an industrial establishment with limited access and only qualified persons will service the installation.

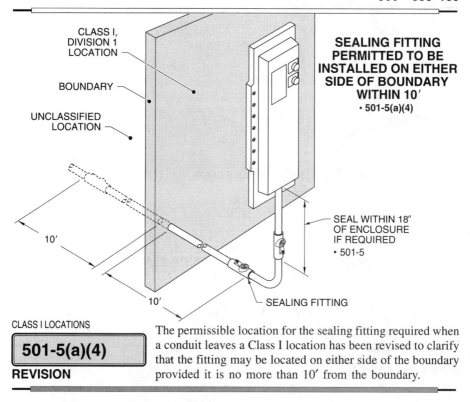

**SEALING FITTING
PERMITTED TO BE
INSTALLED ON EITHER
SIDE OF BOUNDARY
WITHIN 10'**
• 501-5(a)(4)

CLASS I,
DIVISION 1
LOCATION

BOUNDARY

UNCLASSIFIED
LOCATION

SEAL WITHIN 18"
OF ENCLOSURE
IF REQUIRED
• 501-5

SEALING FITTING

10'

10'

CLASS I LOCATIONS

501-5(a)(4)

REVISION

The permissible location for the sealing fitting required when a conduit leaves a Class I location has been revised to clarify that the fitting may be located on either side of the boundary provided it is no more than 10' from the boundary.

**APPROVED EXPLOSIONPROOF
REDUCERS ARE ONLY FITTINGS PERMITTED
BETWEEN SEAL FITTING AND POINT
OF ENTRANCE TO BOUNDARY**
• 501-5(a)(4)

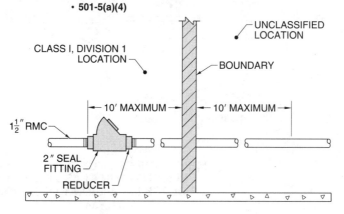

CLASS I LOCATIONS

501-5(a)(4)

REVISION

The requirement that no union, box, fitting, or coupling be located between the sealing fitting and the boundary of a Class I, Division 1 location has been revised to permit approved explosionproof reducers only to be located in that space.

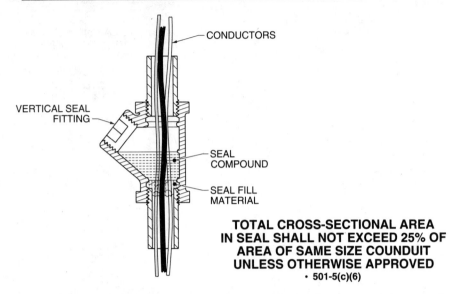

CONDUCTORS

VERTICAL SEAL FITTING

SEAL COMPOUND

SEAL FILL MATERIAL

TOTAL CROSS-SECTIONAL AREA IN SEAL SHALL NOT EXCEED 25% OF AREA OF SAME SIZE COUNDUIT UNLESS OTHERWISE APPROVED
· 501-5(c)(6)

CLASS I LOCATIONS

501-5(c)(6)

NEW SUBSECTION

A new subsection has been added to the requirements for conduit seals in Class I, Division 1 and 2 locations. Conductor fill in the seal is limited to 25% of the cross-sectional area of the conduit of the same size, unless specifically approved for a greater fill.

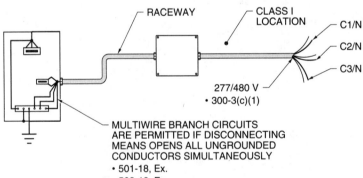

RACEWAY

CLASS I LOCATION

C1/N

C2/N

C3/N

277/480 V
· 300-3(c)(1)

MULTIWIRE BRANCH CIRCUITS ARE PERMITTED IF DISCONNECTING MEANS OPENS ALL UNGROUNDED CONDUCTORS SIMULTANEOUSLY
· 501-18, Ex.
· 502-18, Ex.

MULTIWIRE BRANCH CIRCUITS ARE NOT PERMITTED IN CLASS I, DIVISION 1 OR CLASS II, DIVISION 1 LOCATIONS
· 501-18
· 502-18

CLASS I LOCATIONS

501-18

REVISION

Multiwire branch circuits are not permitted in Class I, Division 1 locations. The same requirement appears in 502-18 for Class II, Division 1 locations.

CLASS II LOCATIONS

502-4(a), Ex.
NEW EXCEPTION

Listed MC cable with a gas/vaportight, continuous, corrugated aluminum sheath and an outer jacket of a suitable polymeric material is permitted to be installed in a Class II, Division 1 location provided it is an industrial establishment with limited access and only qualified persons will service the installation.

CLASS II LOCATIONS

502-8(b)
REVISION

The list of the types of motors and generators permitted in Class II, Division 2 locations has been expanded to permit the use of totally enclosed water-air cooled types provided they maintain the proper external surface temperatures per 500-3(f).

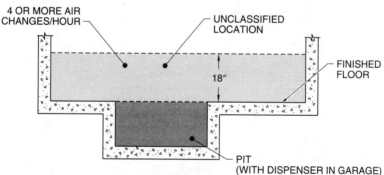

4 OR MORE AIR CHANGES/HOUR

UNCLASSIFIED LOCATION

18″

FINISHED FLOOR

PIT
(WITH DISPENSER IN GARAGE)
• CLASS I, DIVISION 1 LOCATION W/O VENTILATION
• CLASS I, DIVISION 2 LOCATION W/VENTILATION
• 511-3(b)

SPACES UP TO 18″ NOT REQUIRED TO BE CLASSIFIED AS CLASS I, DIVISION 2 IF AHJ IS SATISFIED A MINIMUM OF 4 AIR CHANGES PER HOUR IS PROVIDED
• 511-3(a), Ex.

COMMERCIAL GARAGES, REPAIR AND STORAGE

511-3(a), Ex.
NEW EXCEPTION

Spaces up to 18″ above the floor in commercial garages are not required to be classified if the enforcing agency is satisfied that there is a minimum of four air changes per hour provided by mechanical ventilation.

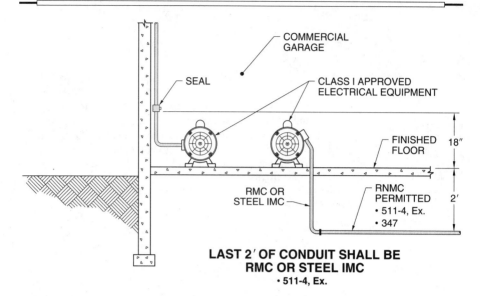

COMMERCIAL
GARAGE

SEAL

CLASS I APPROVED
ELECTRICAL EQUIPMENT

FINISHED
FLOOR

18"

RMC OR
STEEL IMC

RNMC
PERMITTED
• 511-4, Ex.
• 347

2'

**LAST 2' OF CONDUIT SHALL BE
RMC OR STEEL IMC**
• 511-4, Ex.

COMMERCIAL GARAGES,
REPAIR AND STORAGE

511-4, Ex.

NEW EXCEPTION

RNMC is permitted to be used as a wiring method in Class I locations provided it is buried at a depth of at least 2'. RMC or IMC shall be used for the last 2' underground, and to the point of connection or emergence of the above ground raceway.

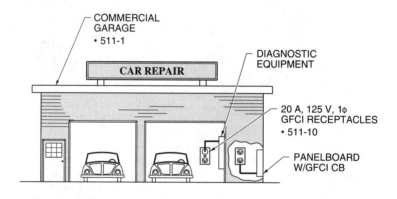

COMMERCIAL
GARAGE
• 511-1

CAR REPAIR

DIAGNOSTIC
EQUIPMENT

20 A, 125 V, 1φ
GFCI RECEPTACLES
• 511-10

PANELBOARD
W/GFCI CB

**ALL 15 OR 20 A, 125 V, 1φ RECEPTACLES
FOR DIAGNOSTIC EQUIPMENT,
HAND TOOLS, OR PORTABLE LIGHTING
SHALL HAVE GFCI PROTECTION**
• 511-10

COMMERCIAL GARAGES,
REPAIR AND STORAGE

511-10

REVISION

All 15 or 20 A, 125 V, 1φ receptacles installed in areas where hand tools, portable lighting equipment, or other diagnostic equipment is used, shall have GFCI protection.

ALL METAL RACEWAYS, METAL-JACKETED CABLES, AND NONCURRENT-CARRYING METAL PARTS SHALL BE GROUNDED PER 250
• 511-16

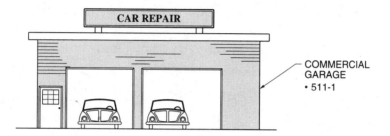

COMMERCIAL GARAGE • 511-1

COMMERCIAL GARAGES, REPAIR AND STORAGE

511-16

NEW SECTION

All metal raceways, metal-jacketed cables, and all noncurrent-carrying metal parts of equipment in commercial garages shall be grounded per 250.

GASOLINE DISPENSING AND SERVICE STATIONS

514-5(a)

REVISION

The general requirements for circuit disconnects at gasoline service stations have been revised to clarify that the disconnecting means shall be clearly identified, readily accessible, and located remote from the dispensing devices.

HEALTH CARE FACILITIES

517-3

NEW DEFINITION

A definition of ambulatory health care center (AHCCs) has been added. *AHCCs* are buildings or parts of buildings designed for treating four or more patients at one time. The services provided in these centers are outpatient care involving surgery, hemodialysis, and other forms of emergency care.

NURSING HOMES AND LIMITED CARE FACILITIES

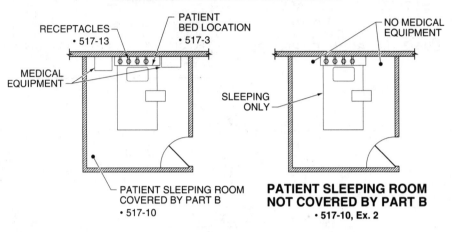

**PATIENT SLEEPING ROOM
NOT COVERED BY PART B**
• 517-10, Ex. 2

517-10, Ex. 2
REVISION

General sleeping areas of nursing homes or limited care facilities are not covered by the wiring methods in 517, Part B if only routine medical services are intended to be performed on the patient.

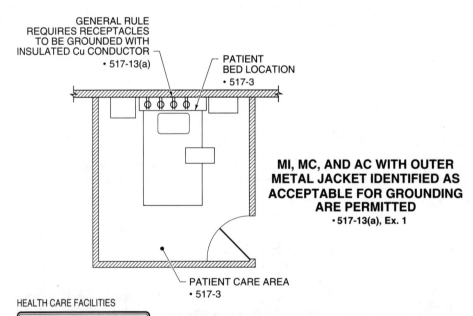

**MI, MC, AND AC WITH OUTER
METAL JACKET IDENTIFIED AS
ACCEPTABLE FOR GROUNDING
ARE PERMITTED**
• 517-13(a), Ex. 1

517-13(a), Ex. 1
REVISION

Listed MI, MC, and AC cables are permitted in lieu of metal raceways, where the outer sheath of the cable is identified for use as an EGC.

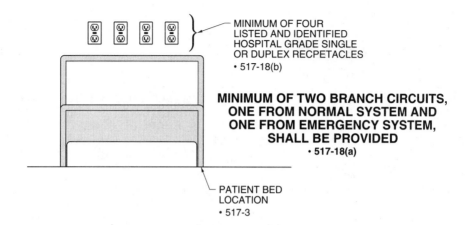

MINIMUM OF FOUR
LISTED AND IDENTIFIED
HOSPITAL GRADE SINGLE
OR DUPLEX RECPETACLES
• 517-18(b)

**MINIMUM OF TWO BRANCH CIRCUITS,
ONE FROM NORMAL SYSTEM AND
ONE FROM EMERGENCY SYSTEM,
SHALL BE PROVIDED**
• 517-18(a)

PATIENT BED
LOCATION
• 517-3

HEALTH CARE FACILITIES

517-18(a)

REVISION

A minimum of two branch circuits shall be provided in patient bed locations in general care areas. One branch circuit shall originate from the emergency system and one from the normal system. The same panelboard shall be used for the source of all normal system branch circuits.

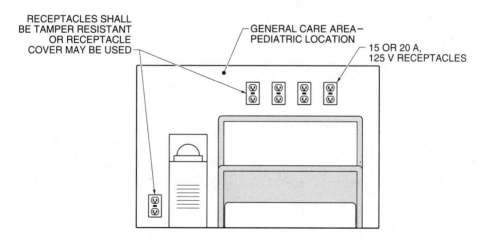

RECEPTACLES SHALL
BE TAMPER RESISTANT
OR RECEPTACLE
COVER MAY BE USED

GENERAL CARE AREA –
PEDIATRIC LOCATION

15 OR 20 A,
125 V RECEPTACLES

**RECEPTACLE COVER PERMITTED IN LIEU
OF TAMPER-RESISTANT RECEPTACLE**
• 517-18(c), Ex.

HEALTH CARE FACILITIES

517-18(c), Ex.

NEW EXCEPTION

A new exception permits the use of receptacle covers, which restrict access to the energized parts of a receptacle, in lieu of tamper-resistant receptacles.

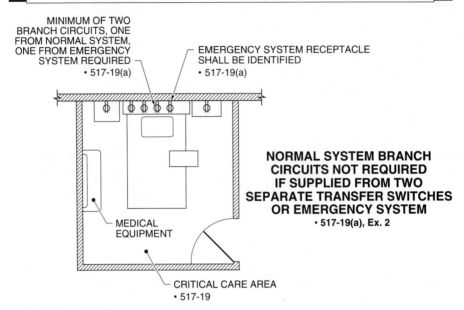

MINIMUM OF TWO
BRANCH CIRCUITS, ONE
FROM NORMAL SYSTEM,
ONE FROM EMERGENCY
SYSTEM REQUIRED
• 517-19(a)

EMERGENCY SYSTEM RECEPTACLE
SHALL BE IDENTIFIED
• 517-19(a)

**NORMAL SYSTEM BRANCH
CIRCUITS NOT REQUIRED
IF SUPPLIED FROM TWO
SEPARATE TRANSFER SWITCHES
OR EMERGENCY SYSTEM**
• 517-19(a), Ex. 2

MEDICAL
EQUIPMENT

CRITICAL CARE AREA
• 517-19

HEALTH CARE FACILITIES

517-19(a), Ex. 2

NEW EXCEPTION

Normal system branch circuits are not required in patient bed locations in critical care areas if the emergency system circuits are provided from two separate transfer switches.

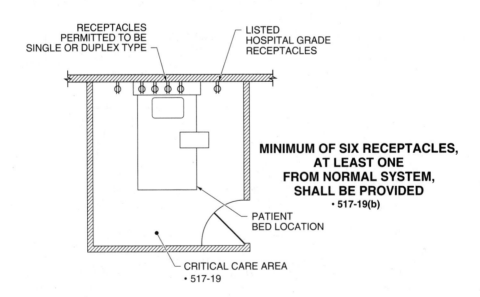

RECEPTACLES
PERMITTED TO BE
SINGLE OR DUPLEX TYPE

LISTED
HOSPITAL GRADE
RECEPTACLES

**MINIMUM OF SIX RECEPTACLES,
AT LEAST ONE
FROM NORMAL SYSTEM,
SHALL BE PROVIDED**
• 517-19(b)

PATIENT
BED LOCATION

CRITICAL CARE AREA
• 517-19

HEALTH CARE FACILITIES

517-19(b)

REVISION

The requirements for patient bed location receptacles in critical care areas have been revised to clarify that the normal system branch circuit required in 517-19(a) shall feed at least one of the six receptacles required in 517-19(b).

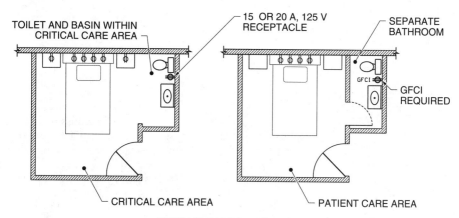

TOILET AND BASIN WITHIN
CRITICAL CARE AREA

15 OR 20 A, 125 V
RECEPTACLE

SEPARATE
BATHROOM

GFCI
REQUIRED

CRITICAL CARE AREA

PATIENT CARE AREA

**GFCI NOT REQUIRED IN
CRITICAL CARE AREAS
HAVING TOILET AND BASIN**
• 517-21

HEALTH CARE FACILITIES

517-21

NEW SECTION

In general, patient bathroom receptacles are required to have GFCI protection. This clarifies that receptacles installed in critical care areas which include a toilet and basin need not be provided with GFCI protection.

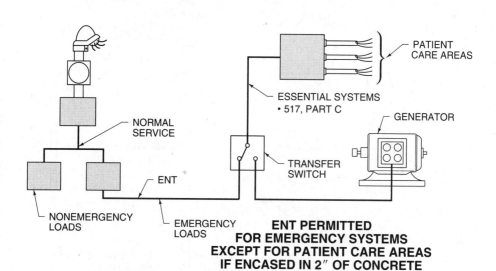

NORMAL
SERVICE

PATIENT
CARE AREAS

ESSENTIAL SYSTEMS
• 517, PART C

GENERATOR

ENT

TRANSFER
SWITCH

NONEMERGENCY
LOADS

EMERGENCY
LOADS

**ENT PERMITTED
FOR EMERGENCY SYSTEMS
EXCEPT FOR PATIENT CARE AREAS
IF ENCASED IN 2″ OF CONCRETE**
• 517-30(c)(3), Ex. 4

HEALTH CARE FACILITIES

**517-30(c)(3),
Ex. 4**

REVISION

ENT encased in at least 2″ of concrete has been added to the list of permissible wiring methods for emergency systems in hospitals provided the wiring does not supply branch circuits in patient care areas.

HEALTH CARE FACILITIES

517-30(c)(3), Ex. 5

NEW EXCEPTION

MI cable has been added to the list of permissible wiring methods for emergency systems in hospitals. MI cable supplying branch circuits in patient care areas shall meet the provisions of 517-13.

HEALTH CARE FACILITIES

517-30(c)(3), Ex. 6

NEW EXCEPTION

Flexible metal raceways and cable assemblies are permitted to be used for emergency system wiring in hospitals when flexible terminations at equipment are necessary or where prefabricated headwalls are used.

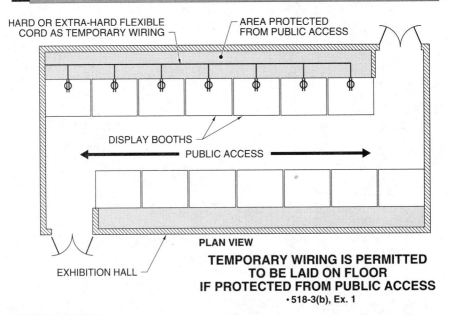

HARD OR EXTRA-HARD FLEXIBLE CORD AS TEMPORARY WIRING

AREA PROTECTED FROM PUBLIC ACCESS

DISPLAY BOOTHS

PUBLIC ACCESS

EXHIBITION HALL

PLAN VIEW

TEMPORARY WIRING IS PERMITTED TO BE LAID ON FLOOR IF PROTECTED FROM PUBLIC ACCESS
• 518-3(b), Ex. 1

PLACES OF ASSEMBLY

518-3(b), Ex. 1

NEW EXCEPTION

Permission to install flexible cables and cords, approved for hard or extra hard usage as temporary wiring on floors, has been removed from the general rule and placed as Ex. 1. The cords and cables shall be protected from contact by the public.

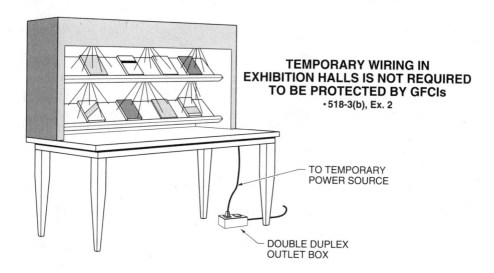

**TEMPORARY WIRING IN
EXHIBITION HALLS IS NOT REQUIRED
TO BE PROTECTED BY GFCIs**
•518-3(b), Ex. 2

TO TEMPORARY
POWER SOURCE

DOUBLE DUPLEX
OUTLET BOX

PLACES OF ASSEMBLY

518-3(b), Ex. 2

NEW EXCEPTION

Temporary wiring in exhibition halls is not required to be provided with GFCI protection specified in 305-6.

PLACES OF ASSEMBLY
• CHURCH CHAPELS
• DINING HALLS
• RESTAURANTS
• CONFERENCE ROOMS
• MEETING ROOMS

WIRING METHODS
ENT OR RNMC
• CONCEALED WITHIN WALLS, FLOORS, CEILINGS, ETC.
• ABOVE SUSPENDED CEILINGS
• 15-MINUTE FINISH RATING

**ENT AND RNMC ARE
PERMITTED IN PLACES
OF ASSEMBLY**
• 518-4, Ex.

PLACES OF ASSEMBLY

518-4, Ex.

NEW EXCEPTION

A new exception has been added to the wiring methods permitted in places of assembly. ENT and RNMC can be installed in church chapels, dining halls, restaurants, and conference or meeting rooms in hotels or motels if it is concealed within walls, floors, ceilings, etc., with a 15 minute finish rating or above suspended ceilings with a 15 minute finish rating.

NEW DEFINITIONS • 520-2

BORDER LIGHT	DROP BOX	FOOTLIGHT
Strip lighting that is permanently installed overhead	Pendant or flush-mounted receptacles installed in a box fed by multiconductor cable	Border lighting that is permanently installed either in or on the stage

PROSCENIUM	STRIP LIGHT	TWO-FER
Wall that separates the stage from the audience or house	Multiple lamps laid out in rows to create a lighting fixture	Device containing one male plug and two female connectors for terminating two loads to one circuit

THEATERS AND
SIMILAR LOCATIONS

520-2
NEW SECTION

A new section covering definitions has been added to 520. Twelve definitions have been added for terms that are industry-specific for theaters and similar locations.

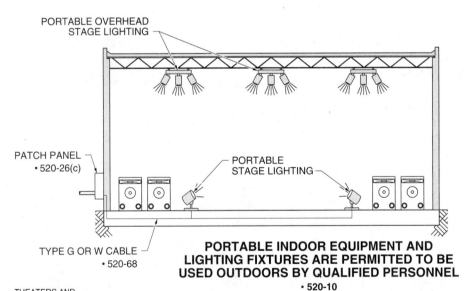

PORTABLE OVERHEAD
STAGE LIGHTING

PATCH PANEL
• 520-26(c)

PORTABLE
STAGE LIGHTING

TYPE G OR W CABLE
• 520-68

PORTABLE INDOOR EQUIPMENT AND LIGHTING FIXTURES ARE PERMITTED TO BE USED OUTDOORS BY QUALIFIED PERSONNEL
• 520-10

THEATERS AND
SIMILAR LOCATIONS

520-10
NEW SECTION

This new section permits portable indoor equipment, such as stage lighting and power distribution equipment, to be used outdoors temporarily, if attended with qualified personnel and protected against unauthorized access.

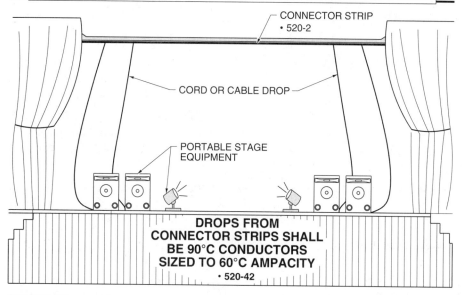

CONNECTOR STRIP
• 520-2

CORD OR CABLE DROP

PORTABLE STAGE
EQUIPMENT

**DROPS FROM
CONNECTOR STRIPS SHALL
BE 90°C CONDUCTORS
SIZED TO 60°C AMPACITY**
• 520-42

THEATERS AND
SIMILAR LOCATIONS

520-42

REVISION

Drops from connector strips shall consist of 90°C conductors sized at the 60°C ampacity.

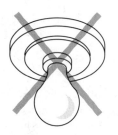

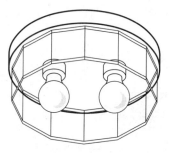

**BARE LAMPS
ARE NOT PERMITTED
IN SCENERY UNLESS
2″CLEARANCE FROM
COMBUSTIBLE MATERIALS**
• 520-47

**GUARDED
LAMPS
PERMITTED**
• 520-47

**DECORATIVE
LAMPS
IN SCENERY
PERMITTED**
• 520-47, Ex.

**LAMPS IN SCENERY AREAS
SHALL BE GUARDED**
• 520-47

THEATERS AND
SIMILAR LOCATIONS

520-47

REVISION

The requirement that lamps in scenery areas be guarded has been extended to all areas behind the stage which might come in contact with the scenery. This includes all backstage areas, including ancillary areas.

THEATERS AND
SIMILAR LOCATIONS

520-47, Ex.

NEW EXCEPTION

This new exception permits bare bulbs or lamps to be installed without a 2″ clearance from combustible material or where subject to physical damage if they are installed in the scenery.

THEATERS AND
SIMILAR LOCATIONS

520-53(k)

REVISION

Paralleled sets of conductors which feed equipment shall be marked to indicate the presence of paralleled internal connections.

THEATERS AND
SIMILAR LOCATIONS

520-67

REVISION

The section has been revised to clarify that the requirements of the section only apply to multipole branch-circuit cable connectors. In addition, the requirement that the connector be rated in amperes and be polarized has been revised to indicate these requirements only apply to multipole connectors.

CARNIVALS, CIRCUSES, FAIRS,
AND SIMILAR EVENTS

525

NEW ARTICLE

This new article contains installation requirements for electrical systems in carnivals, fairs, circuses, and similar locations. The requirements also include all wiring in or on structures.

CARNIVALS

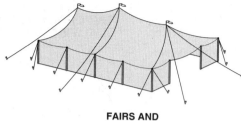

**FAIRS AND
CIRCUSES**

**TRAVELLING
SHOWS**

WIRING METHODS PERMITTED

• CHAPTER 1– 4 METHODS
• FLEXIBLE CORDS AND CABLES
• LISTED EXTRA-HARD USAGE
• LISTED WET LOCATIONS
• SUNLIGHT RESISTANT

CARNIVALS, CIRCUSES, FAIRS,
AND SIMILAR EVENTS

525-13(a)

NEW SECTION

Wiring methods for carnivals, fairs, etc., shall be a recognized method from NEC® Chapters 1 – 4. Flexible cords and cables are permitted if they are listed for extra-hard usage and wet locations and are sunlight resistant.

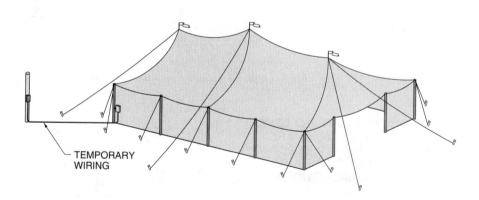

TEMPORARY
WIRING

**GFCI PROTECTION NOT REQUIRED
FOR TEMPORARY WIRING FOR CARNIVALS,
CIRCUSES, FAIRS, AND SIMILAR EVENTS**
• 525-18

CARNIVALS, CIRCUSES, FAIRS,
AND SIMILAR EVENTS

525-18

NEW SECTION

Temporary wiring for carnivals, fairs, etc., is not required to be provided with GFCI protection per 305-6.

PORTABLE EQUIPMENT PERMITTED FOR TEMPORARY USE OUTDOORS IF OPERATED BY QUALIFIED PERSONS AND ACCESS IS LIMITED
• 530-6

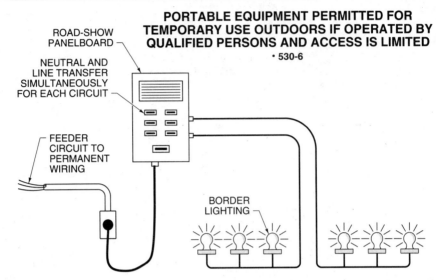

ROAD-SHOW PANELBOARD

NEUTRAL AND LINE TRANSFER SIMULTANEOUSLY FOR EACH CIRCUIT

FEEDER CIRCUIT TO PERMANENT WIRING

BORDER LIGHTING

MOTION PICTURE AND TELEVISION STUDIOS AND SIMILAR LOCATIONS

530-6

NEW SECTION

This new section permits portable indoor equipment, such as stage lighting and power distribution equipment, to be used outdoors temporarily, if attended by qualified personnel and protected against unauthorized access.

SEPARATELY DERIVED SYSTEM • 530, PART G	
WIRING METHODS	• 530-71
VOLTAGE DROP	• 530-71(d)
GROUNDING	• 530-72
RECEPTACLES	• 530-73

SEPARATELY DERIVED 120 V, 1ϕ, 3-WIRE SYSTEMS ARE PERMITTED TO SUPPLY ELECTRONIC EQUIPMENT TO REDUCE OBJECTIONABLE NOISE
• 530-70

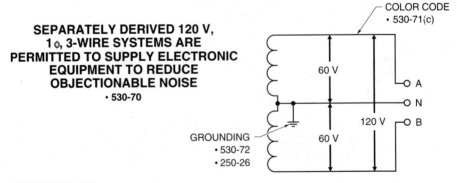

COLOR CODE
• 530-71(c)

60 V

○ A

○ N

120 V ○ B

GROUNDING
• 530-72
• 250-26

60 V

120 V, 1ϕ, 3-WIRE DERIVED SYSTEM

MOTION PICTURE AND TELEVISION STUDIOS AND SIMILAR LOCATIONS

530-70

NEW PART

A new Part G contains requirements for separately derived systems with 60 V to ground. These systems can be used to reduce objectional noise in electronic equipment locations.

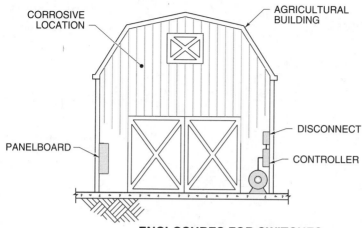

**ENCLOSURES FOR SWITCHES
CBs, FUSES, ETC. INSTALLED
IN CORROSIVE ATMOSPHERES
SHALL BE SUITABLE FOR USE**
• 547-5(b)

AGRICULTURAL BUILDINGS

547-5(b)

REVISION

Enclosures for switches, CBs, controllers, and fuses installed in corrosive atmospheres in agricultural buildings shall be suitable for the conditions of use.

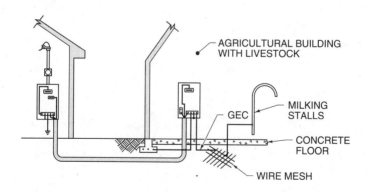

**WIRE MESH OR OTHER CONDUCTIVE ELEMENTS SHALL BE
INSTALLED IN CONCRETE FLOORS AND BONDED TO GES**
• 547-8(b)

AGRICULTURAL BUILDINGS

547-8(b)

REVISION

Wire mesh or other conductive elements shall be installed in concrete floors of livestock areas to meet grounding and bonding requirements. The mesh or conductive elements shall be bonded to the building GES.

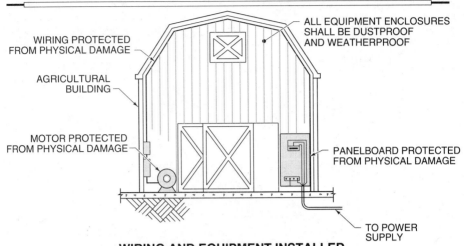

WIRING PROTECTED FROM PHYSICAL DAMAGE

AGRICULTURAL BUILDING

MOTOR PROTECTED FROM PHYSICAL DAMAGE

ALL EQUIPMENT ENCLOSURES SHALL BE DUSTPROOF AND WEATHERPROOF

PANELBOARD PROTECTED FROM PHYSICAL DAMAGE

TO POWER SUPPLY

WIRING AND EQUIPMENT INSTALLED IN AREAS WITH EXCESSIVE DUST OR CORROSIVE ATMOSPHERES SHALL BE PROTECTED AGAINST PHYSICAL DAMAGE
• 547-10

AGRICULTURAL BUILDINGS

547-10
REVISION

Wiring and equipment installed in agricultural buildings shall be protected from physical damage when installed in areas subjected to excessive dust or corrosive atmospheres.

MOBILE HOMES, MANUFACTURED HOMES, AND MOBILE HOME PARKS

550-1
REVISION

The title and scope of this article have been revised to clarify that mobile home parks, in addition to mobile homes and manufactured homes, are included in 550.

MOBILE HOMES, MANUFACTURED HOMES, AND MOBILE HOME PARKS

550-2, FPN
REVISION

The FPN has been revised to clarify that both gas ranges and electric ranges are to be included in the definition of portable appliances.

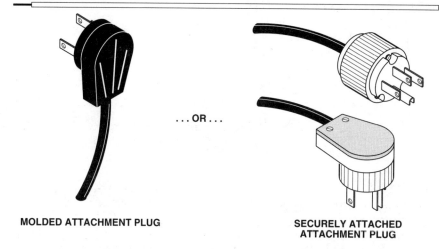

MOLDED ATTACHMENT PLUG

. . . OR . . .

SECURELY ATTACHED ATTACHMENT PLUG

FEEDER SUPPLY ATTACHMENT PLUGS ARE NOT REQUIRED TO BE ONLY INTEGRALLY MOLDED TYPE
• 550-5(a)

MOBILE HOMES,
MANUFACTURED HOMES,
AND MOBILE HOME PARKS

550-5(a)

REVISION

The requirement that feeder supply cords be supplied with an integrally molded attachment plug has been revised. Securely attached plug caps are now permitted in lieu of molded attachment plugs.

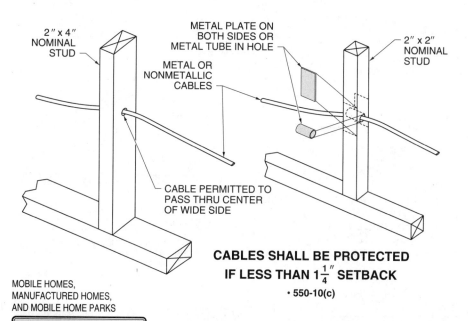

2″ x 4″ NOMINAL STUD

METAL PLATE ON BOTH SIDES OR METAL TUBE IN HOLE

METAL OR NONMETALLIC CABLES

2″ x 2″ NOMINAL STUD

CABLE PERMITTED TO PASS THRU CENTER OF WIDE SIDE

CABLES SHALL BE PROTECTED IF LESS THAN $1\frac{1}{4}''$ SETBACK
• 550-10(c)

MOBILE HOMES,
MANUFACTURED HOMES,
AND MOBILE HOME PARKS

550-10(c)

REVISION

The required setback, for both metal and nonmetallic cables, from the edge of framing members has been reduced from $1\frac{1}{2}''$ to $1\frac{1}{4}''$ to correlate with 300-4.

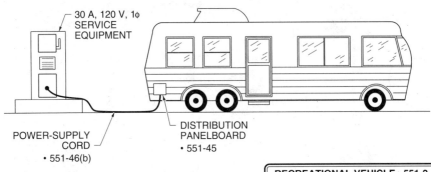

30 A, 120 V, 1φ
SERVICE
EQUIPMENT

DISTRIBUTION
PANELBOARD
• 551-45

POWER-SUPPLY
CORD
• 551-46(b)

**IF TWO TO FIVE BRANCH
CIRCUITS ARE INSTALLED,
SERVICE SHALL BE
30 A, 120 V, 1φ**
• 551-42(c)

RECREATIONAL VEHICLE • 551-2
• VEHICULAR-TYPE UNIT
• TEMPORARY LIVING
• PULLED BY ANOTHER VEHICLE
 OR SELF-POWERED
• RECREATIONAL USE

RECREATIONAL VEHICLES
AND RECREATIONAL
VEHICLE PARKS

551-42(c)

REVISION

The branch circuit calculation for recreational vehicles has been revised to clarify that if two to five 15 or 20 A circuits are used, the service shall be a 30 A, 120 V, 1φ power supply assembly.

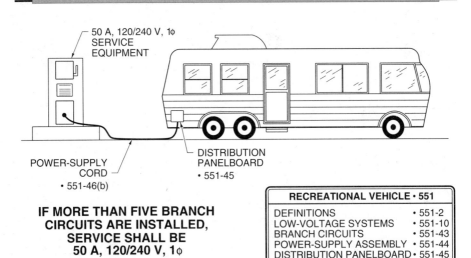

50 A, 120/240 V, 1φ
SERVICE
EQUIPMENT

DISTRIBUTION
PANELBOARD
• 551-45

POWER-SUPPLY
CORD
• 551-46(b)

**IF MORE THAN FIVE BRANCH
CIRCUITS ARE INSTALLED,
SERVICE SHALL BE
50 A, 120/240 V, 1φ**
• 551-42(d)

RECREATIONAL VEHICLE • 551

DEFINITIONS	• 551-2
LOW-VOLTAGE SYSTEMS	• 551-10
BRANCH CIRCUITS	• 551-43
POWER-SUPPLY ASSEMBLY	• 551-44
DISTRIBUTION PANELBOARD	• 551-45
WIRING METHODS	• 551-47
GROUNDING	• 551-54

RECREATIONAL VEHICLES
AND RECREATIONAL
VEHICLE PARKS

551-42(d)

REVISION

The branch circuit calculation for recreational vehicles has been revised to clarify that if more than five 15 or 20 A circuits are used, the service shall be a 50 A, 120/240 V, 1φ power supply assembly.

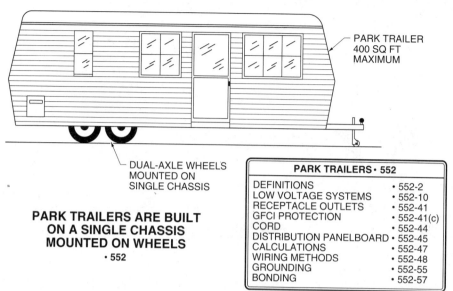

PARK TRAILER
400 SQ FT
MAXIMUM

DUAL-AXLE WHEELS
MOUNTED ON
SINGLE CHASSIS

**PARK TRAILERS ARE BUILT
ON A SINGLE CHASSIS
MOUNTED ON WHEELS**
• **552**

PARK TRAILERS • 552	
DEFINITIONS	• 552-2
LOW VOLTAGE SYSTEMS	• 552-10
RECEPTACLE OUTLETS	• 552-41
GFCI PROTECTION	• 552-41(c)
CORD	• 552-44
DISTRIBUTION PANELBOARD	• 552-45
CALCULATIONS	• 552-47
WIRING METHODS	• 552-48
GROUNDING	• 552-55
BONDING	• 552-57

PARK TRAILERS

552

NEW ARTICLE

This new article contains requirements for electrical conductors and equipment installed in or on park trailers. Park trailers are mounted on wheels and have a total area of not more than 400 sq ft.

PARK TRAILERS

552-43(a)

NEW SECTION

The power supply to park trailers is required to be either a listed 30 A or listed 50 A power supply cord with an integral molded cap, or a feeder which is permanently installed.

PARK TRAILERS

552-48(a)

NEW SECTION

Wiring methods permitted for park trailers are RMC, IMC, EMT, RNMC, FMC, and MC, MI, NM, and AC cable. Acceptable EGCs are listed in 250-91.

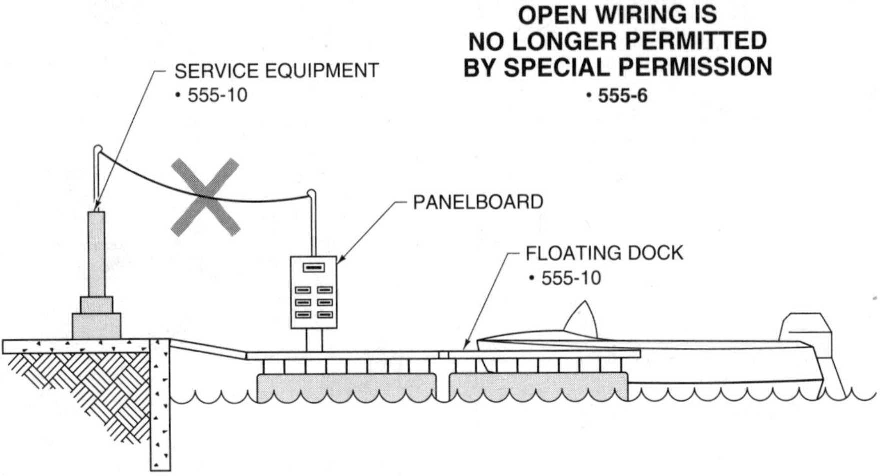

**OPEN WIRING IS
NO LONGER PERMITTED
BY SPECIAL PERMISSION**
• 555-6

SERVICE EQUIPMENT
• 555-10

PANELBOARD

FLOATING DOCK
• 555-10

MARINAS AND BOATYARDS

555-6

REVISION

The permission to use open wiring in marinas and boatyards has been deleted from this section. In addition, FPN 1 which contained the requirements for obtaining special permission to use open wiring, has been deleted.

ELECTRIC SIGNS AND
OUTLINE LIGHTING

600

REVISION

This article has been completely revised for better understanding and ease of use. A FPN has been added following the scope to clarify that all products and installations using neon tubing are covered.

ELECTRIC SIGNS AND
OUTLINE LIGHTING

600-2

NEW SECTION

A *sign body* is the part of the sign that is not designed for electrical connections, but for protection from the weather.

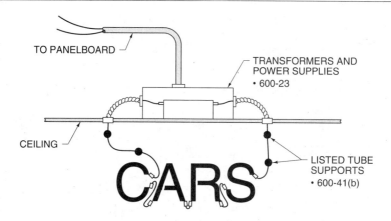

TO PANELBOARD

TRANSFORMERS AND
POWER SUPPLIES
• 600-23

CEILING

LISTED TUBE
SUPPORTS
• 600-41(b)

CARS

**SKELETON TUBING IS NEON TUBING THAT FORMS A
SIGN WITHOUT USE OF AN ENCLOSURE OR SIGN BODY**
• 600-2

ELECTRIC SIGNS AND
OUTLINE LIGHTING

600-2
NEW DEFINITION

Skeleton tubing is any neon tubing that is either the sign itself, or outline lighting which is not attached to the sign body or enclosure.

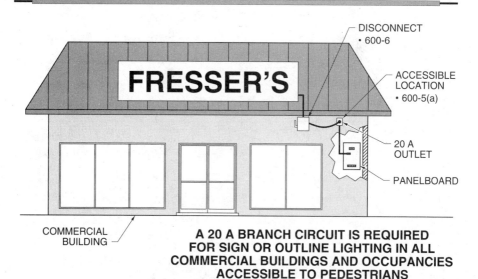

DISCONNECT
• 600-6

FRESSER'S

ACCESSIBLE
LOCATION
• 600-5(a)

20 A
OUTLET

PANELBOARD

COMMERCIAL
BUILDING

**A 20 A BRANCH CIRCUIT IS REQUIRED
FOR SIGN OR OUTLINE LIGHTING IN ALL
COMMERCIAL BUILDINGS AND OCCUPANCIES
ACCESSIBLE TO PEDESTRIANS**
• 600-5(a)

ELECTRIC SIGNS AND
OUTLINE LIGHTING

600-5(a)
REVISION

The requirements for a required branch circuit for a sign outlet in commercial buildings has been revised. A dedicated circuit of at least 20 A shall be provided in an outlet at an accessible location for each building or tenant space.

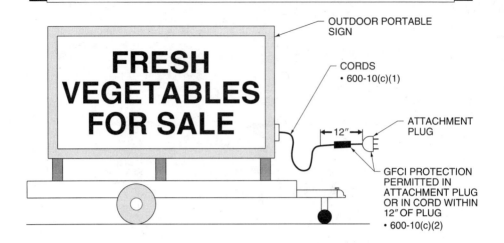

OUTDOOR PORTABLE SIGN

CORDS
• 600-10(c)(1)

ATTACHMENT PLUG

GFCI PROTECTION PERMITTED IN ATTACHMENT PLUG OR IN CORD WITHIN 12″ OF PLUG
• 600-10(c)(2)

ALL OUTDOOR PORTABLE SIGNS, REGARDLESS OF LOCATION, SHALL HAVE GFCI PROTECTION
• 600-10(c)(2)

ELECTRIC SIGNS AND
OUTLINE LIGHTING

600-10(c)(2)

REVISION

GFCI protection shall be an integral part of the attachment plug, or installed in the supply cord within 12″ from the attachment plug.

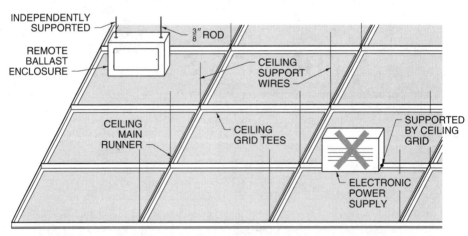

INDEPENDENTLY SUPPORTED

$\frac{3}{8}$″ ROD

REMOTE BALLAST ENCLOSURE

CEILING SUPPORT WIRES

CEILING MAIN RUNNER

CEILING GRID TEES

SUPPORTED BY CEILING GRID

ELECTRONIC POWER SUPPLY

BALLASTS, ELECTRONIC POWER SUPPLIES, AND TRANSFORMERS ARE PERMITTED TO BE INSTALLED ABOVE SUSPENDED CEILINGS BUT CANNOT BE SUPPORTED BY CEILING GRID
• 600-21(f)

ELECTRIC SIGNS AND
OUTLINE LIGHTING

600-21(f)

NEW SECTION

Enclosures for remote ballasts, transformers, and other electronic equipment are permitted to be installed above a suspended ceiling provided they are not supported by the ceiling grid.

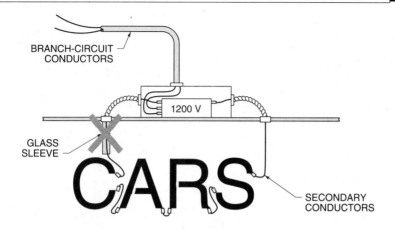

**GLASS SLEEVING IS NO LONGER
PERMITTED AS A WIRING METHOD
FOR NEON CONDUCTORS OVER 1000 V**
• 600-32(a)

ELECTRIC SIGNS AND
OUTLINE LIGHTING

600-32(a)
REVISION

Wiring methods for field-installed skeleton tubing have been revised by deleting the permission to use glass sleeving as an acceptable wiring method for skeleton tubing conductors.

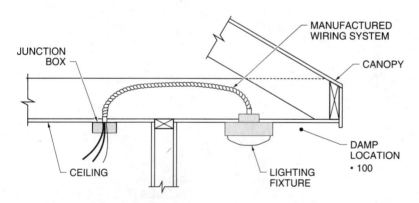

**LISTED MANUFACTURED WIRING
SYSTEMS ARE PERMITTED
TO BE USED OUTDOORS**
• 604-4, Ex. 2

MANUFACTURED WIRING SYSTEMS• 604	
DEFINITION	• 604-2
USES PERMITTED	• 604-4
USES NOT PERMITTED	• 604-5
CONSTRUCTION	• 604-6
UNUSED OUTLETS	• 604-7

MANUFACTURED
WIRING SYSTEMS

604-4, Ex. 2
NEW EXCEPTION

This new exception permits manufactured wiring systems to be used outdoors if they are listed for the purpose.

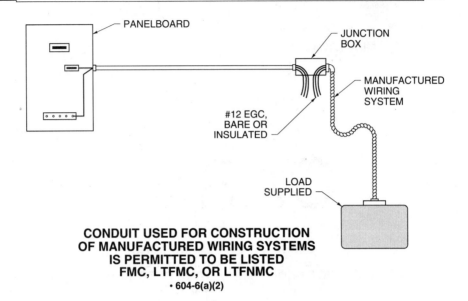

**CONDUIT USED FOR CONSTRUCTION
OF MANUFACTURED WIRING SYSTEMS
IS PERMITTED TO BE LISTED
FMC, LTFMC, OR LTFNMC**
• 604-6(a)(2)

WIRING SYSTEMS

604-6(a)(2)

REVISION

Construction provisions for manufactured wiring systems
have been revised to clarify that the only permissible conduit
types are listed FMC, LTFMC, or LTFNMC with the proper
size and type of EGC.

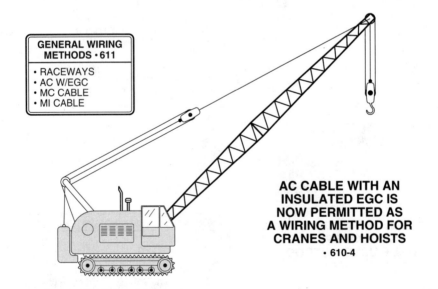

**GENERAL WIRING
METHODS • 611**

• RACEWAYS
• AC W/EGC
• MC CABLE
• MI CABLE

**AC CABLE WITH AN
INSULATED EGC IS
NOW PERMITTED AS
A WIRING METHOD FOR
CRANES AND HOISTS**
• 610-4

CRANES AND HOISTS

610-11

REVISION

AC cable, with an insulated EGC, has been added to the
list of permissible wiring methods for cranes and hoists.

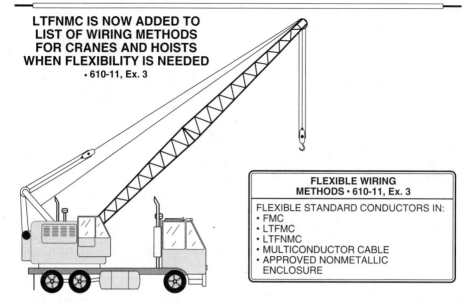

**LTFNMC IS NOW ADDED TO
LIST OF WIRING METHODS
FOR CRANES AND HOISTS
WHEN FLEXIBILITY IS NEEDED**
• 610-11, Ex. 3

**FLEXIBLE WIRING
METHODS • 610-11, Ex. 3**

FLEXIBLE STANDARD CONDUCTORS IN:
• FMC
• LTFMC
• LTFNMC
• MULTICONDUCTOR CABLE
• APPROVED NONMETALLIC
 ENCLOSURE

CRANES AND HOISTS

610-11, Ex. 3

REVISION

This exception has been revised to permit the use of LTFNMC to be used where flexible connections are necessary, such as at motor terminal housings and similar equipment.

ELEVATORS, DUMBWAITERS,
ESCALATORS, ETC.

620

REVISION

This article has been completely rewritten. In addition, 620-2 which contains many definitions, has been added.

ELEVATORS, DUMBWAITERS,
ESCALATORS, ETC.

620-5

REVISION

Workspace clearance requirements have been revised by re-location to this new section and by removal of the exceptions. Essentially, the provisions of 110-16(a) can be waived through the use of flexible connections, guards, low voltage, or equipment that does not require servicing.

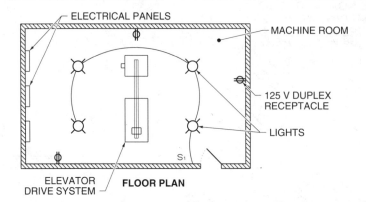

ELECTRICAL PANELS

MACHINE ROOM

125 V DUPLEX RECEPTACLE

LIGHTS

ELEVATOR DRIVE SYSTEM

FLOOR PLAN

> **BRANCH-CIRCUIT REQUIREMENTS • 620-23**
> - DEDICATED CIRCUIT FOR RECEPTACLES/LIGHTS
> - LIGHTING NOT CONNECTED TO LOAD SIDE OF GFCI RECEPTACLE
> - LIGHT SWITCH AT POINT OF ENTRY
> - AT LEAST ONE 125 V DUPLEX RECEPTACLE

ELEVATORS, DUMBWAITERS, ESCALATORS, ETC.

620-23

NEW SECTION

This new section contains all requirements for branch circuits in machine rooms/machinery space. Among the new requirements are a separate branch circuit shall supply lighting and receptacles in these spaces.

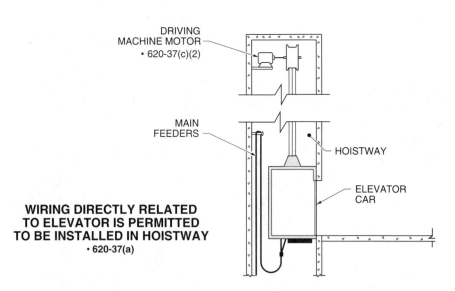

DRIVING MACHINE MOTOR
• 620-37(c)(2)

MAIN FEEDERS

HOISTWAY

ELEVATOR CAR

WIRING DIRECTLY RELATED TO ELEVATOR IS PERMITTED TO BE INSTALLED IN HOISTWAY
• 620-37(a)

ELEVATORS, DUMBWAITERS, ESCALATORS, ETC.

620-37(a)

REVISION

The provisions for wiring in hoistways and machine rooms have been revised. Only wiring directly associated with the elevator or dumbwaiter, including associated systems, fire alarm, communications, etc., are permitted inside the hoistway or machine room.

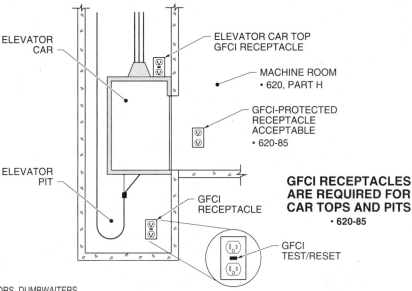

ELEVATOR CAR

ELEVATOR CAR TOP
GFCI RECEPTACLE

MACHINE ROOM
• 620, PART H

GFCI-PROTECTED
RECEPTACLE
ACCEPTABLE
• 620-85

ELEVATOR
PIT

GFCI
RECEPTACLE

**GFCI RECEPTACLES
ARE REQUIRED FOR
CAR TOPS AND PITS**
• 620-85

GFCI
TEST/RESET

ELEVATORS, DUMBWAITERS,
ESCALATORS, ETC.

620-85
REVISION

All 125 V, 15 or 20 A, 1φ receptacles on elevator car tops, in machinery spaces, pits, and in escalator and moving walkways shall be provided from GFCI receptacles only.

ELECTRIC VEHICLE
CHARGING SYSTEM EQUIPMENT

625
NEW ARTICLE

This new article covering electric vehicle charging systems has been added. Sections covering definitions, wiring methods, equipment construction, control and protection, and equipment locations have been included.

INFORMATION
TECHNOLOGY EQUIPMENT

645
REVISION

The title of 645 has been changed to "Information Technology Equipment." This change reflects the term used in many international standards.

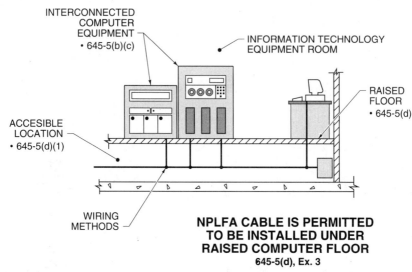

INTERCONNECTED COMPUTER EQUIPMENT
• 645-5(b)(c)

INFORMATION TECHNOLOGY EQUIPMENT ROOM

RAISED FLOOR
• 645-5(d)

ACCESIBLE LOCATION
• 645-5(d)(1)

WIRING METHODS

NPLFA CABLE IS PERMITTED TO BE INSTALLED UNDER RAISED COMPUTER FLOOR
645-5(d), Ex. 3

INFORMATION TECHNOLOGY EQUIPMENT

645-5(d), Ex. 3

REVISION

The exception for other cables permitted to be installed under raised floors of computer rooms has been revised. In addition to the cables already permitted, nonpower limited fire alarm cable (NPLFA) is now permitted for signaling systems.

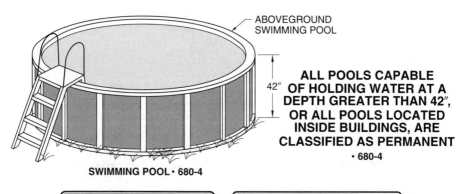

ABOVEGROUND SWIMMING POOL

ALL POOLS CAPABLE OF HOLDING WATER AT A DEPTH GREATER THAN 42", OR ALL POOLS LOCATED INSIDE BUILDINGS, ARE CLASSIFIED AS PERMANENT
• 680-4

42"

SWIMMING POOL • 680-4

PERMANENTLY INSTALLED	STORABLE
• INGROUND OR ON GROUND • INSIDE OF BUILDING • WATER DEPTH GREATER THAN 42"	• ON OR ABOVEGROUND • MAXIMUM DEPTH OF 42" • NONMETALLIC MOLDED WALLS • INFLATABLE

SWIMMING POOLS, FOUNTAINS, AND SIMILAR INSTALLATIONS

680-4

REVISION

The definition of *permanently installed swimming, wading, and therapeutic pools* has been revised. All pools, capable of holding water at a depth greater than 42" are now classified as permanent, regardless if they can be readily disassembled for storage.

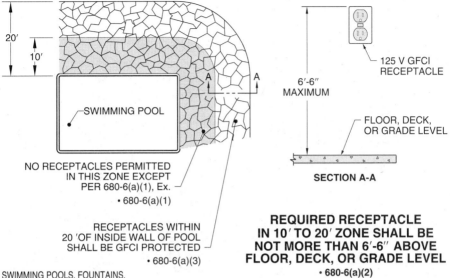

20′

10′

SWIMMING POOL

125 V GFCI
RECEPTACLE

6′-6″
MAXIMUM

FLOOR, DECK,
OR GRADE LEVEL

SECTION A-A

NO RECEPTACLES PERMITTED
IN THIS ZONE EXCEPT
PER 680-6(a)(1), Ex.
• 680-6(a)(1)

RECEPTACLES WITHIN
20 ′OF INSIDE WALL OF POOL
SHALL BE GFCI PROTECTED
• 680-6(a)(3)

**REQUIRED RECEPTACLE
IN 10′ TO 20′ ZONE SHALL BE
NOT MORE THAN 6′-6″ ABOVE
FLOOR, DECK, OR GRADE LEVEL**
• 680-6(a)(2)

SWIMMING POOLS, FOUNTAINS,
AND SIMILAR LOCATIONS

680-6(a)(2)

REVISION

The requirements for a 125 V receptacle in the 10′ to 20′ range from the inside wall of the pool has been revised to clarify that the receptacle shall be installed not more than 6′-6″ above the floor grade level or platform.

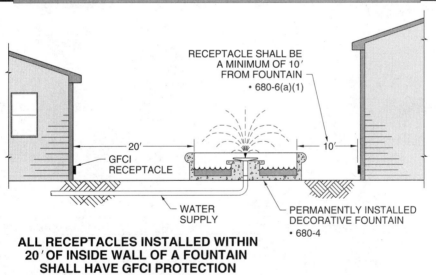

RECEPTACLE SHALL BE
A MINIMUM OF 10′
FROM FOUNTAIN
• 680-6(a)(1)

20′

10′

GFCI
RECEPTACLE

WATER
SUPPLY

PERMANENTLY INSTALLED
DECORATIVE FOUNTAIN
• 680-4

**ALL RECEPTACLES INSTALLED WITHIN
20′ OF INSIDE WALL OF A FOUNTAIN
SHALL HAVE GFCI PROTECTION**
• 680-6(a)(3)

SWIMMING POOLS, FOUNTAINS,
AND SIMILAR LOCATIONS

680-6(a)(3)

REVISION

The provision that receptacles located within 20′ of the inside wall of a pool be GFCI protected has been revised. The requirement now applies to receptacles within 20′ of fountains as well as pools.

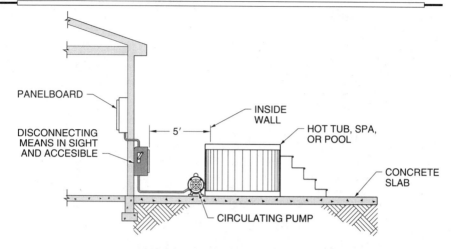

**DISCONNECTS FOR POOLS, SPAS, OR
HOT TUBS SHALL BE LOCATED AT
LEAST 5′ HORIZONTALLY FROM INSIDE WALL**
• **680-12**

SWIMMING POOLS, FOUNTAINS,
AND SIMILAR INSTALLATIONS

680-12

NEW SECTION

Part A now contains general disconnect requirements for all pools, spas, or hot tubs. All disconnects shall be located within sight, shall be accessible, and shall be located at least 5′ horizontally from the inside wall of the pool, spa, or hot tub.

**LTFNMC IS NOW PERMITTED
TO BE USED FOR
WET-NICHE FIXTURES**
• **680-20(b)(1)**

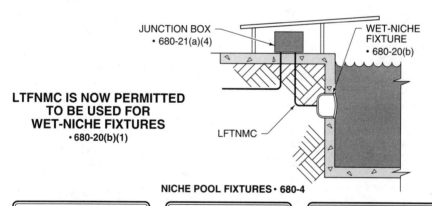

NICHE POOL FIXTURES • 680-4

DRY-NICHE FIXTURE	**NO-NICHE FIXTURE**	**WET-NICHE FIXTURE**
• INSTALLED IN WALL OF POOL OR FOUNTAIN • SEALED AGAINST ENTRY OF WATER	• INSTALLED ABOVE OR BELOW WATER	• INSTALLED IN FORMING SHELL • COMPLETELY SURROUNDED BY WATER

SWIMMING POOLS, FOUNTAINS,
AND SIMILAR LOCATIONS

680-20(b)(1)

REVISION

The list of permissible wiring methods for wet-niche fixtures has been expanded. RMC, RNMC, IMC, and LTFNMC are now permitted.

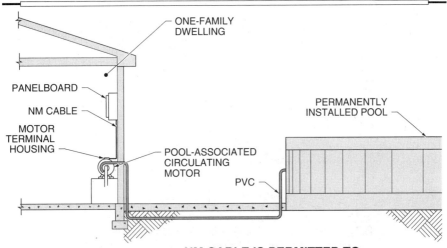

**NM CABLE IS PERMITTED TO
SUPPLY MOTORS LOCATED IN INTERIOR
OF ONE-FAMILY DWELLINGS**
• 680-25(c), Ex. 3

SWIMMING POOLS, FOUNTAINS,
AND SIMILAR INSTALLATIONS

680-25(c), Ex. 3
REVISION

The exception, which permits any Chapter 3 wiring method to supply a motor located in the interior of a one-family dwelling, has been revised. The revision clarifies that NMC is permitted to supply pool-associated motors.

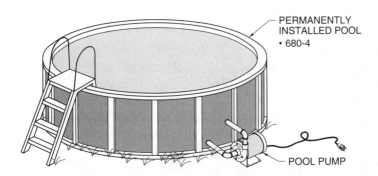

**LISTED CORD- AND PLUG-CONNECTED
POOL PUMPS INCORPORATING AN
APPROVED DOUBLE INSULATION SYSTEM
ARE PERMITTED FOR PERMANENTLY
INSTALLED POOLS**
• 680-28

SWIMMING POOLS, FOUNTAINS,
AND SIMILAR INSTALLATIONS

680-28
NEW SECTION

Double insulated pools pumps, for permanently installed pools, are now permitted to be installed provided they are listed, cord- and plug-connected, and constructed of an approved system of double insulation.

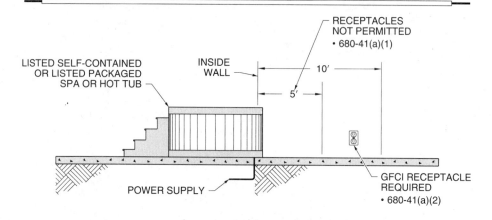

LISTED SELF-CONTAINED OR LISTED PACKAGED SPA OR HOT TUB

INSIDE WALL

RECEPTACLES NOT PERMITTED
• 680-41(a)(1)

POWER SUPPLY

GFCI RECEPTACLE REQUIRED
• 680-41(a)(2)

**POWER SUPPLY NOT REQUIRED TO BE GFCI PROTECTED
IF INTEGRAL GFCI PROTECTION IS PROVIDED
FOR ALL ELECTRICAL COMPONENTS WITHIN UNIT**
• 680-42, Ex.

SWIMMING POOLS, FOUNTAINS, AND SIMILAR LOCATIONS

680-42, Ex.

NEW EXCEPTION

The GFCI protection requirements for spas and hot tubs have been revised. Outlets for self-contained spas or hot tubs, or packaged spas or hot tubs, shall have GFCI protection unless the listed package or self-contained unit contains integral GFCI protection.

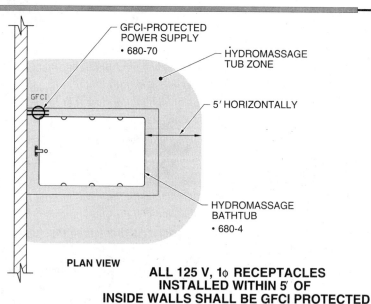

GFCI-PROTECTED POWER SUPPLY
• 680-70

HYDROMASSAGE TUB ZONE

GFCI

5′ HORIZONTALLY

HYDROMASSAGE BATHTUB
• 680-4

PLAN VIEW

**ALL 125 V, 1φ RECEPTACLES
INSTALLED WITHIN 5′ OF
INSIDE WALLS SHALL BE GFCI PROTECTED**
• 680-70

SWIMMING POOLS, FOUNTAINS, AND OTHER LOCATIONS

680-70

REVISION

The requirements for GFCI protection for hydromassage bathtubs have been revised. All 125 V, 1φ receptacles located within 5′ of the inside walls of a hydromassage tub shall have GFCI protection.

SOLAR
PHOTOVOLTAIC SYSTEMS

690-2
REVISION

The term power conditioning unit has been changed to inverter, which is a more commonly used term than power conditioning unit. An *inverter* converts DC input to AC output.

FIRE PUMPS

695
NEW ARTICLE

This new article incorporates many of the existing rules concerning fire pumps and some installation requirements from NFPA 20 into a single article. Unlike emergency systems in 700, a connection ahead of the service disconnecting means is a permitted power source for fire pumps.

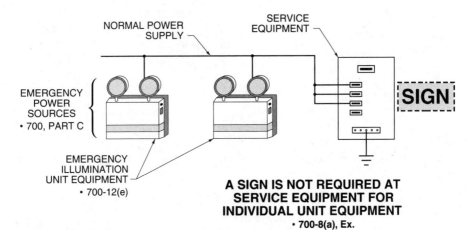

EMERGENCY SYSTEMS

NORMAL POWER SUPPLY

SERVICE EQUIPMENT

EMERGENCY POWER SOURCES
• 700, PART C

EMERGENCY ILLUMINATION UNIT EQUIPMENT
• 700-12(e)

SIGN

A SIGN IS NOT REQUIRED AT SERVICE EQUIPMENT FOR INDIVIDUAL UNIT EQUIPMENT
• **700-8(a), Ex.**

EMERGENCY SYSTEMS

700-8(a), Ex.
NEW EXCEPTION

In general, on-site emergency power sources shall be marked by a sign placed at the service entrance equipment. This new exception permits individual unit equipment, per 700-12(e), to be installed without a sign at the service equipment.

**EMERGENCY SYSTEM WIRING AND NORMAL SYSTEM
WIRING SHALL BE KEPT INDEPENDENT OF EACH OTHER**
• **700-9(b)**

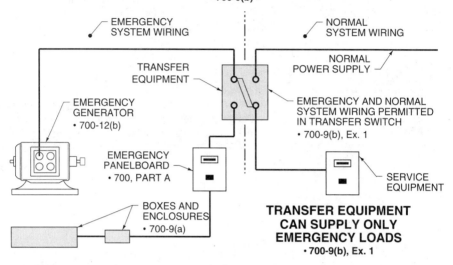

TRANSFER EQUIPMENT
CAN SUPPLY ONLY
EMERGENCY LOADS
• 700-9(b), Ex. 1

EMERGENCY SYSTEMS

700-9(b), Ex. 1
REVISION

The requirement for separation of normal system conductors and emergency system conductors has been modified. The two system conductors are permitted in the same transfer switch and the transfer switch can serve only emergency loads.

FEEDER CIRCUIT WIRING FOR . . .

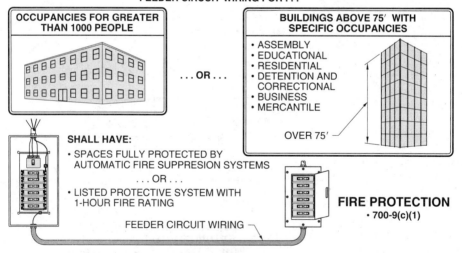

FIRE PROTECTION
• 700-9(c)(1)

EMERGENCY SYSTEMS

700-9(c)(1)
NEW SUBSECTION

This new subsection has been added for assembly occupancies for greater than 1000 persons or for buildings above 75′ with any of the following occupancies: assembly, educational, residential, detention and correctional, business or mercantile. Feeder-circuit wiring installed in these locations shall be protected by approved automatic fire suppression systems or by a listed protective system with a 1-hour fire rating.

FEEDER CIRCUIT EQUIPMENT FOR . . .

OCCUPANCIES FOR GREATER THAN 1000 PEOPLE

. . . OR . . .

BUILDINGS ABOVE 75′ WITH SPECIFIC OCCUPANCIES

• ASSEMBLY
• EDUCATIONAL
• RESIDENTIAL
• DETENTION AND CORRECTIONAL
• BUSINESS
• MERCANTILE

OVER 75′

SHALL HAVE:

• SPACES FULLY PROTECTED BY AUTOMATIC FIRE SUPPRESION SYSTEMS
. . . OR . . .
• SPACES WITH 1-HOUR FIRE RESISTANCE RATING

FIRE PROTECTION
• 700-9(c)(2)

PANELBOARDS TRANSFORMERS TRANSFER SWITCHES

EMERGENCY SYSTEMS

700-9(c)(2)

NEW SUBSECTION

Equipment for feeder circuits installed in assembly occupancies for greater than 1000 persons or for buildings with occupancy uses such as assembly, educational, residential, detention and correctional, business, or mercantile shall be protected by an approved automatic fire suppression system or be installed in spaces with a 1-hour fire resistance rating. The same requirement applies to equipment for emergency sources of power per 700-12(a – d).

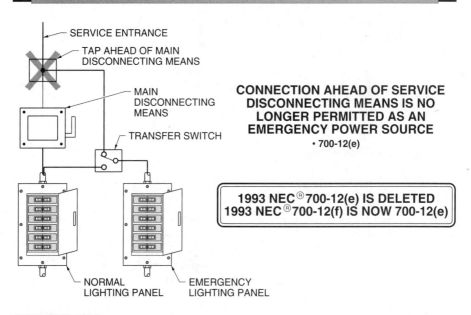

SERVICE ENTRANCE
TAP AHEAD OF MAIN DISCONNECTING MEANS
MAIN DISCONNECTING MEANS
TRANSFER SWITCH

CONNECTION AHEAD OF SERVICE DISCONNECTING MEANS IS NO LONGER PERMITTED AS AN EMERGENCY POWER SOURCE
• 700-12(e)

1993 NEC® 700-12(e) IS DELETED
1993 NEC® 700-12(f) IS NOW 700-12(e)

NORMAL LIGHTING PANEL   EMERGENCY LIGHTING PANEL

EMERGENCY SYSTEMS

700-12(e)

DELETION

Subsection (e) covering the requirements for connecting ahead of the service disconnecting means for an emergency power source has been deleted. Subpart (f) covering unit equipment has been renamed subpart (e).

LEGALLY REQUIRED STANDBY SYSTEMS ARE INTENDED TO SUPPLY, DISTRIBUTE, AND CONTROL ELECTRICITY WHEN NORMAL POWER IS INTERRUPTED
• 701-1

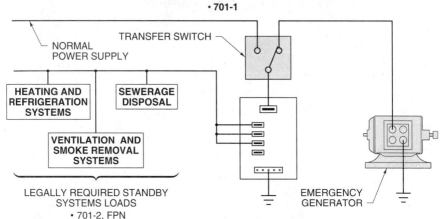

LEGALLY REQUIRED
STANDBY SYSTEMS

701-1

REVISION

The scope has been revised by deleting the word "design" from the text. Legally required standby systems supply power automatically to selected loads that are not supplied by the emergency system.

LEGALLY REQUIRED STANDBY SYSTEMS

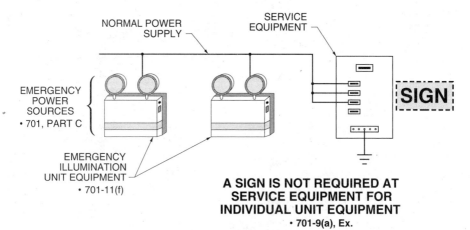

LEGALLY REQUIRED
STANDBY SYSTEMS

701-9(a), Ex.

NEW EXCEPTION

On-site legally required standby power sources are required to be identified by a sign placed at the service entrance equipment. This new exception permits individual unit equipment per 701-11(f) to be installed without a sign at the service equipment.

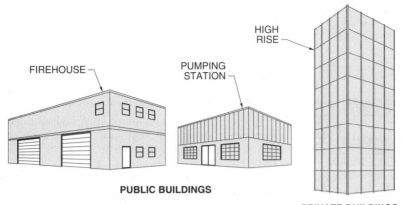

PUBLIC BUILDINGS

HIGH
RISE

FIREHOUSE

PUMPING
STATION

PRIVATE BUILDINGS

OPTIONAL STANDBY SYSTEMS • 702-2
• PUBLIC OR PRIVATE FACILITIES
• LIFE SAFETY NOT THREATENED
• ON-SITE GENERATED POWER
• MANUAL OR AUTOMATIC TRANSFER

**OPTIONAL STANDBY SYSTEMS
MAY BE INSTALLED IN EITHER
PUBLIC OR PRIVATE FACILITIES**
• 702-2

OPTIONAL STANDBY SYSTEMS

702-2

REVISION

The definition of optional standby systems has been revised to clarify that these systems may be installed in either private or public facilities. Optional standby systems typically supply loads to which the interruption of power would result in discomfort but not loss of life.

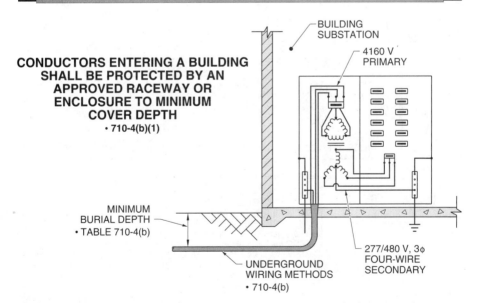

BUILDING
SUBSTATION

4160 V
PRIMARY

**CONDUCTORS ENTERING A BUILDING
SHALL BE PROTECTED BY AN
APPROVED RACEWAY OR
ENCLOSURE TO MINIMUM
COVER DEPTH**
• 710-4(b)(1)

MINIMUM
BURIAL DEPTH
• TABLE 710-4(b)

277/480 V, 3φ
FOUR-WIRE
SECONDARY

UNDERGROUND
WIRING METHODS
• 710-4(b)

OVER 600 VOLTS,
NOMINAL, GENERAL

710-4(b)(1)

REVISION

The requirements for protection against damage for underground conductors, over 600 V, have been modified. Conductors that emerge from the ground shall be protected down to the minimum cover depth in Table 710-4(b), instead of just to the ground line.

OVER 600 VOLTS,
NOMINAL, GENERAL

710-4(b)(2), Ex.

NEW EXCEPTION

This new exception permits splices of engineered cable systems to be interrupted and overlapped if the conductors are single conductor cables with metallic shields and proper spacing between phases is maintained.

CLASS 1, CLASS 2, AND CLASS 3
REMOTE-CONTROL, SIGNALING,
AND POWER-LIMITED CIRCUITS

725

REVISION

The requirements for Class 1, 2, and 3 circuits for remote-control, signaling, and power-limited circuits have been completely rewritten for better clarity and understanding. The article has also been extensively reorganized to make the application of the rules easier to follow.

DEFINTIONS · 725-2

CLASS 1 CIRCUIT	CLASS 2 CIRCUIT
• LOCATED ON LOAD SIDE OF OCPD OR POWER-LIMITED SOURCE AND EQUIPMENT • VOLTAGE AND POWER LIMITATION OF SOURCE PER 725-21	• LOCATED ON LOAD SIDE OF A CLASS 2 POWER SOURCE AND EQUIPMENT • CONSIDERS SAFETY FROM A FIRE INITIATION POINT OF VIEW AND PROTECTION AGAINST ELECTRICAL SHOCK

CLASS 3 CIRCUIT
• LOCATED ON LOAD SIDE OF A CLASS 3 POWER SOURCE AND EQUIPMENT • CONSIDERS SAFETY FROM A FIRE INITIATION POINT OF VIEW WITH AN INCREASED EMPHASIS ON PREVENTION OF ELECTRICAL SHOCK

CLASS 1, CLASS 2, AND CLASS 3
REMOTE-CONTROL, SIGNALING,
AND POWER-LIMITED CIRCUITS

725-2

NEW SECTION

This new section on definitions has been added. Definitions are provided for Class 1, 2, and 3 circuits.

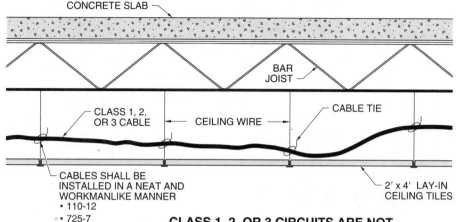

CONCRETE SLAB

BAR JOIST

CLASS 1, 2, OR 3 CABLE

CEILING WIRE

CABLE TIE

CABLES SHALL BE INSTALLED IN A NEAT AND WORKMANLIKE MANNER
• 110-12
• 725-7

2′ x 4′ LAY-IN CEILING TILES

CLASS 1, 2, OR 3 CIRCUITS ARE NOT PERMITTED TO BE INSTALLED IN A MANNER WHICH WILL SUBJECT CABLES TO PHYSICAL DAMAGE
• 725-7

CLASS 1, CLASS 2, AND CLASS 3 REMOTE CONTROL, SIGNALING, AND POWER-LIMITED CIRCUITS

725-7

NEW SECTION

This new section requires that the installation of all Class 1, 2, and 3 circuits be installed in a neat and workmanlike manner. Cables shall be installed so they are not subject to damage by normal building use.

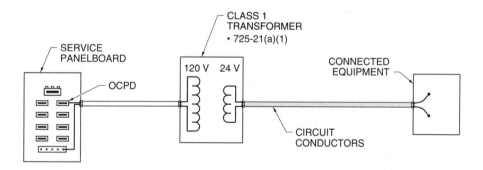

CLASS 1 TRANSFORMER
• 725-21(a)(1)

SERVICE PANELBOARD

OCPD

120 V   24 V

CONNECTED EQUIPMENT

CIRCUIT CONDUCTORS

CLASS 1 CIRCUIT CONDUCTORS ARE NOT SUBJECT TO DERATING FACTORS OF 310-15
• 725-23

CLASS 1, CLASS 2, AND CLASS 3 REMOTE-CONTROL, SIGNALING, AND POWER-LIMITED CIRCUITS

725-23

REVISION

The requirements for overcurrent protection for Class 1 circuits have been revised to clarify that the derating provisions listed in 310-15 do not apply. Other derating provisions in 725-27 and 725-28 apply accordingly.

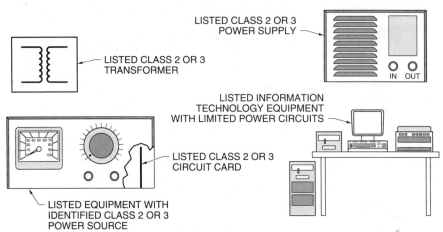

POWER SOURCES FOR CLASS 2 AND 3 CIRCUITS NOW INCLUDE LISTED INFORMATION TECHNOLOGY POWER CIRCUITS
• 725-41(a)

CLASS 1, CLASS 2, AND CLASS 3, REMOTE-CONTROL, SIGNALING AND POWER-LIMITED CIRCUITS

725-41(a)
NEW SUBSECTION

The list of permitted power sources for Class 2 and Class 3 circuits has been expanded to include limited power circuits from information technology equipment. A FPN has been added to point out that such circuits are used to interconnect information technology equipment.

CABLE INSTALLATION – HAZARDOUS LOCATIONS • 725-61(d)

CABLE	SUPPORT	LOCATION PERMITTED
• PLTC POWER-LIMITED TRAY CABLE	• CABLE TRAYS • RACEWAYS • MESSENGER WIRE • **OTHER ADEQUATE SUPPORT MEANS**	• CLASS I, DIVISION 2 501-4(d) • CLASS II, DIVISION 2 502-4 (b) • INTRINSICALLY SAFE CIRCUITS 504-20

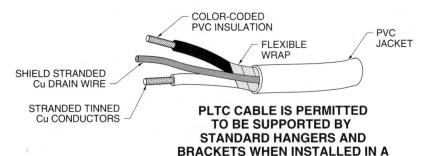

PLTC CABLE IS PERMITTED TO BE SUPPORTED BY STANDARD HANGERS AND BRACKETS WHEN INSTALLED IN A PERMITTED HAZARDOUS LOCATION

CLASS 1, CLASS 2, AND CLASS 3 REMOTE-CONTROL, SIGNALING AND POWER-LIMITED CIRCUITS.

725-61(d)
REVISION

The requirements for installing PLTC in hazardous locations have been revised. Where permitted, PLTC cable may be installed using hangers or brackets provided it is adequately supported.

FIRE ALARM SYSTEMS

760

REVISION

The title of this article has been changed from Fire Protective Signaling Systems to Fire Alarm Systems. In addition, the scope of the article has been changed to include many of the newer fire technology systems.

FIRE ALARM SYSTEMS

760-2

NEW SECTION

This new section includes some of the definitions used exclusively in 760. Definitions are provided for *fire alarm circuit, NPLFA,* and *PLFA.*

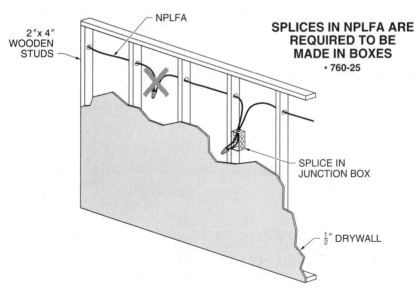

**SPLICES IN NPLFA ARE
REQUIRED TO BE
MADE IN BOXES**
• 760-25

NPLFA

2″ x 4″
WOODEN
STUDS

SPLICE IN
JUNCTION BOX

$\frac{1}{2}″$ DRYWALL

FIRE ALARM SYSTEMS

760-25

REVISION

The requirements for installing NPLFA circuits have been modified to clarify that the wiring methods shall be per 300-15(b) and Chapter 3. This clarifies that boxes are required for NPLFA circuits.

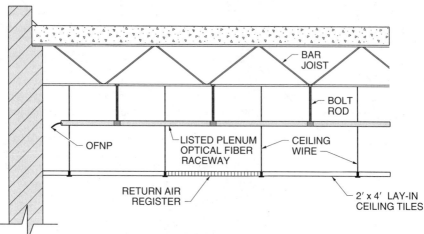

**ONLY OFNP CABLE IS PERMITTED TO BE
INSTALLED IN LISTED PLENUM RACEWAYS**
• 770-53(a)

OPTICAL FIBER
CABLES AND RACEWAYS

770-53(a)

REVISION

The provisions for installing listed optical fiber cables and raceways have been revised. When plenum optical fiber raceways are installed in ducts and plenums per 300-22(b) and 300-22(c), only OFNP cable is permitted.

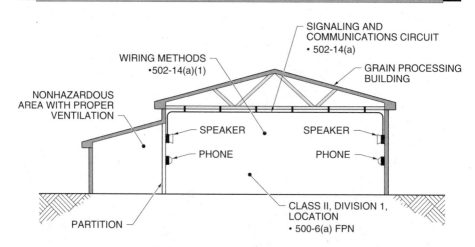

**COMMUNICATIONS CIRCUITS INSTALLED
IN HAZARDOUS LOCATIONS SHALL
COMPLY WITH CHAPTER 5 PROVISIONS**
• 800-7

COMMUNICATIONS CIRCUITS

800-7

NEW SECTION

This new section has been added to the general requirements for communications circuits. Communications circuits installed in hazardous locations shall comply with the applicable provisions of Chapter 5.

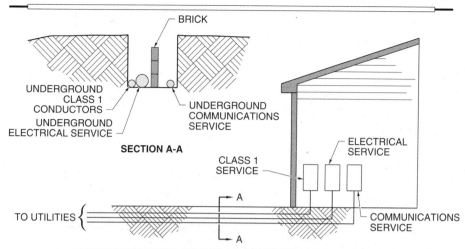

BRICK

UNDERGROUND CLASS 1 CONDUCTORS

UNDERGROUND ELECTRICAL SERVICE

UNDERGROUND COMMUNICATIONS SERVICE

SECTION A-A

CLASS 1 SERVICE

ELECTRICAL SERVICE

TO UTILITIES

A

A

COMMUNICATIONS SERVICE

**UNDERGROUND COMMUNICATIONS CIRCUITS SHALL
BE SEPARATED FROM CLASS 1 AND NPLFA CIRCUITS,
AS WELL AS ELECTRIC LIGHT OR POWER CONDUCTORS**
• 800-11(a)

COMMUNICATIONS CIRCUITS

800-11(a)

REVISION

The requirements for separation of underground communications wiring from electric light or power conductors has been revised. Underground communication wiring shall maintain separation from Class 1 and NPLFA circuits as well.

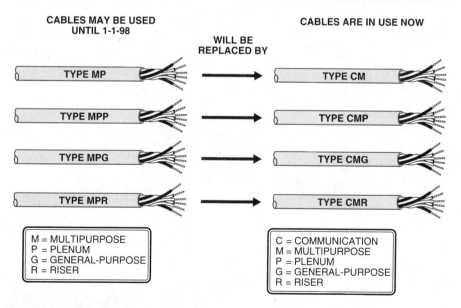

**CABLES MAY BE USED
UNTIL 1-1-98**

CABLES ARE IN USE NOW

**WILL BE
REPLACED BY**

TYPE MP → TYPE CM

TYPE MPP → TYPE CMP

TYPE MPG → TYPE CMG

TYPE MPR → TYPE CMR

M = MULTIPURPOSE
P = PLENUM
G = GENERAL-PURPOSE
R = RISER

C = COMMUNICATION
M = MULTIPURPOSE
P = PLENUM
G = GENERAL-PURPOSE
R = RISER

COMMUNICATIONS CIRCUITS

800-51(g)

REVISION

MPP, MPG, MPR, and MP cables are being replaced as multipurpose cables suitable for communication wiring. CMP, CMR, CMG, and CM cables will replace these cables after January 1, 1998.

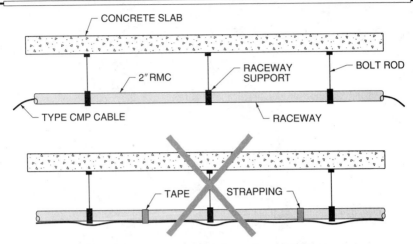

**COMMUNICATION CABLES AND WIRING ARE
PERMITTED TO BE INSTALLED IN RACEWAYS
BUT NOT ON EXTERIOR OF RACEWAY**
• 800-52(e)

COMMUNICATIONS CIRCUITS

800-52(e)

REVISION

The requirements for support of communication conductors and cables have been revised to clarify that communication conductors or cables shall not be attached to, or supported by, the exterior of any raceway.

RADIO AND
TEVEVISION EQUIPMENT

810-12

REVISION

The support requirements for outdoor antennas and lead-in conductors have been modified. Lead-in conductors, in addition to antennas, are not permitted to be supported by the electrical service mast.

RADIO AND
TELEVISION EQUIPMENT

810-21

REVISION

This revision clarifies that when the grounding conductor is installed in a metal raceway, both ends of the raceway shall be bonded to the grounding conductor or to the same terminal or electrode to which the grounding conductor is connected.

CONDUCTOR FILL COMPARISONS

CONDUIT OR TUBING	TABLE 4 OVER 2 WIRES 40% IN SQ IN.			APPENDIX C MAXIMUM NUMBER OF CONDUCTORS, #12 THHN Cu		
	$\frac{1}{2}''$	$\frac{3}{4}''$	$1''$	$\frac{1}{2}''$	$\frac{3}{4}''$	$1''$
EMT	.122	.213	.346	9	16	26
ENT	.099	.181	.314	7	13	23
FMC	.127	.213	.327	9	16	24
IMC	.137	.235	.384	10	17	29
LTFMC	.125	.216	.349	9	16	26
RMC	.125	.220	.355	9	16	26
PVC, SCHEDULE 80	.087	.164	.275	6	12	20
PVC, SCHEDULE 40	.114	.203	.333	8	15	25
LTFNMC–TYPE A	.125	.214	.341	9	16	25
LTFNMC–TYPE B	.125	.216	.349	9	16	26

PVC, SCHEDULE 80

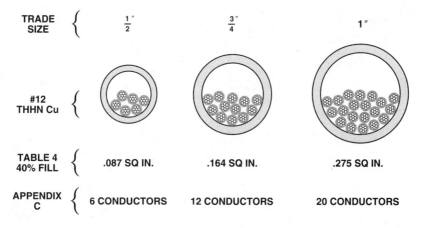

TRADE SIZE	$\frac{1}{2}''$	$\frac{3}{4}''$	$1''$
#12 THHN Cu			
TABLE 4 40% FILL	.087 SQ IN.	.164 SQ IN.	.275 SQ IN.
APPENDIX C	6 CONDUCTORS	12 CONDUCTORS	20 CONDUCTORS

**MAXIMUM NUMBER OF CONDUCTORS
PERMITTED IN A CONDUIT OR TUBING
IS NOW SELECTED BY TYPE OF RACEWAY
SELECTED FOR INSTALLATION**
• APPENDIX C, TABLES C1– C12

CHAPTER 9,
TABLES AND EXAMPLES

APPENDIX C

NEW APPENDIX

Tables 2, 3A, 3B, and 3C have been deleted. Appendix C has been added in their place. Appendix C contains a revised set of tables for determining the maximum number of conductors permitted in conduit and tubing. Each of the respective conduits and tubings has its own table to reflect the different internal diameters of the raceways.

APPENDIX

ABBREVIATIONS			
A	Amps	ITCB	Inverse Time Circuit Breaker
A/C	Air Conditioner	K	Conductor Resistivity
AC	Alternating Current	k	Kilo (1000)
AEGCP	Assured Equipment Grounding Program	kcmil	1000 Circular Mils
		kFT	1000'
A/H	Air Handler	kVA	Kilovolt Amps
AHCC	Ambulatory Health Care Center	kW	Kilowatt
AHJ	Authority Having Jurisdiction	kWh	Kilowatt-Hour
AL	Aluminum	L	Line
AWG	American Wire Gauge	LFLI	Less-Flammable, Liquid-Insulated
C	Celsius		
CB	Circuit Breaker	LP	Lighting Panel
CM	Circular Mils	LRA	Locked-Rotor Ampacity
CMP	Codemaking Panel	LRC	Locked-Rotor Current
Cu	Copper	MBCSCGF	Motor Branch-Circuit, Short-Circuit, Ground-Fault
DC	Direct Current		
DIA	Diameter	NEC®	National Electrical Code®
DP	Double Pole	N	Neutral
E	Voltage	NEMA	National Electrical Manufacturers Association
E_{ff}	Efficiency		
EGC	Equipment Grounding Conductor	NFPA	National Fire Protection Association
Ex.	Exception	NTDF	Non-Time Delay Fuse
F	Fahrenheit	OCPD	Overcurrent Protection Device
FPN	Fine Print Note	OSHA	Occupational Safety and Health Administration
FLA	Full-Load Amps		
FLC	Full-Load Current	P	Power
G	Ground	PF	Power Factor
GR	Green	R	Resistance; Resistor
GEC	Grounding Electrode Conductor	SF	Service Factor
		SP	Single-Pole
GES	Grounding Electrode System	SPCB	Single-Pole Circuit Breaker
GFCI	Ground Fault Circuit Interrupter	sq ft	Square Foot (Feet)
GFPE	Ground Fault Protection of Equipment	SWD	Switched Disconnect
		T	Time
HACR	Heating, Air-Conditioning, Refrigeration	TDF	Time-Delay Fuse
		UF	Underground Feeder
HP	Horsepower	V	Volts
I	Current	VA	Volt Amps
IEC	International Electrotechnical Commission	VD	Voltage Drop
		W	Watts
IG	Isolated Ground	W	White
IN.	Inch	WP	Weatherproof
ITB	Instantaneous Trip Circuit Breaker		

WIRING MATERIALS

AC	Armored Cable	NMC	Nonmetallic-Sheathed Cable (dry or damp)
BX	Trade Name for AC		
EMT	Electrical Metallic Tubing	NPLFA	Nonpower-Limited Fire Alarm Circuit
ENT	Electrical Nonmetallic Tubing		
FMC	Flexible Metal Conduit	OFNP	Nonconductive Optical Fiber Plenum Cable
IGS	Integrated Gas Spacer Cable		
IMC	Intermediate Metal Conduit	PLFA	Power-Limited Fire Alarm Circuit
LTFMC	Liquidtight Flexible Metal Conduit	PLTC	Power-Limited Tray Cable
		PVC	Polyvinyl Chloride
LTFNMC	Liquidtight Flexible Nonmetallic Conduit	RMC	Rigid Metallic Conduit
		RNMC	Rigid Nonmetallic Conduit
MC	Metal-Clad Cable	SE	Service-Entrance Cable
MI	Mineral Insulated Metal-Sheathed Cable	SNM	Shielded Nonmetallic-Sheathed Cable
NM	Nonmetallic-Sheathed Cable (dry)	TC	Tray Cable
		USE	Underground Service-Entrance Cable

SYMBOLS

ELECTRICAL		DRAFTING	
GFCI		BREAK LINE (LONG)	
GROUND		BREAK LINE (PIPE)	
OUTLET		BREAK LINE (SHORT)	
PHASE		CINDER FILL	
SERVICE EQUIPMENT		CONCRETE	
		CUTTING PLANE	
SWITCH		EARTH	
TRANSFORMER		MASONRY WALL	
VIOLATION		WALL SECTION	

RELATED MATERIAL

NEC®-Related Books and Material from American Tech . . .

Text   1558-2
Instructor's Guide   1559-0

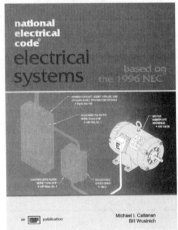

Text   1690-2
Instructor's Guide   1691-0

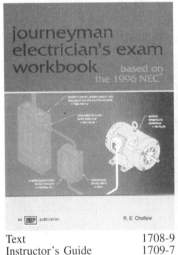

Text   1708-9
Instructor's Guide   1709-7

Text   1530-2

Text   1504-3

Related Books and Material from American Tech . . .

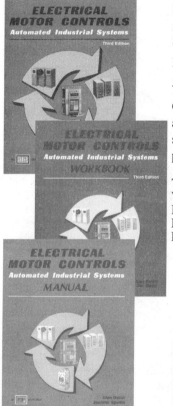

ELECTRICAL MOTOR CONTROLS
Automated Industrial Systems
3rd Edition

By Gary Rockis, Glen Mazur

Industry Approved

526 pages, 738 illustrations, hard cover.

Completely updated with state-of-the-art technology and applications. Programmable controllers and solid state electronic control devices are thoroughly presented. All new Activity Manual.

Text	1666-X
Workbook	1667-8
Instructor's Guide (Workbook)	1669-4
Manual	1668-6
Instructor's Guide (Manual)	1670-8

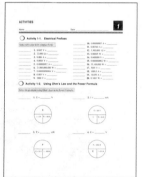

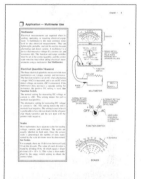

SOLID STATE FUNDAMENTALS
FOR ELECTRICIANS
2nd Edition

By Gary Rockis

232 pages, 481 illustrations, hard cover.

Covers construction, operation, and application of solid state components used in industry. Provides a good background in solid state.

Text	1631-7
Workbook	1632-5
Instructor's Guide	1633-3

Current and Comprehensive

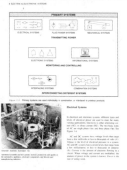

ELECTRICAL/ELECTRONIC SYSTEMS

By Glen A. Mazur, Thomas E. Proctor

490 pages, heavily illustrated, hard cover.

Electrical/Electronic Systems offers a comprehensive introduction to the concepts of electrical and electronic systems. The concise text approaches electrical and electronic circuits and components from a systems standpoint. All elements of residential, commercial, and industrial systems are presented in an easy-to-understand format. Four-color photographs and CAD-drawn illustrations help present the fundamental concepts and skills necessary to successfully compete in today's electrical/electronic field.

Text	1772-0
Workbook	1773-9
Instructor's Guide	1774-7
Transparencies	1771-2

Electrical/Electronic Systems Workbook reinforces information presented in *Electrical/ Electronic Systems*. The Tech-Cheks contain questions based on the corresponding chapter of the textbook. The Worksheets apply electrical and electronic theory to practical problems.

16 Tech-Cheks
132 Worksheets

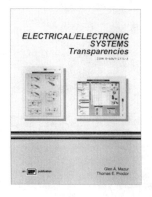

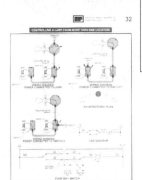

42 four-color transparencies

ELECTRICAL/ELECTRONIC FUNDAMENTALS VIDEO SERIES

By Glen A. Mazur

Features Fluke Meters

Electrical/Electronic Fundamentals Video Series consists of seven four-color videos which present basic electrical theory, safety, digital multimeter principles, and an introduction to fundamental troubleshooting procedures. The videos feature the latest Fluke Corporation electrical testing equipment used in various industrial applications.

Electrical/Electronic Fundamentals Video Series	1406-3
Electrical Principles 1	1407-1
Electrical Principles 2	1408-X
Symbols and Circuits	1409-8
Electrical Safety	1410-1
Digital Multimeters-Basic Measurements	1411-X
Digital Multimeters-Advanced Measurements	1412-8
Digital Multimeters-Testing Procedures	1413-6
Electrical/Electronic Fundamentals Workbook	1414-4
Electrical/Electronic Fundamentals Workbook Instructor's Guide	1415-2

Electrical/Electronic Fundamentals Workbook enhances principles and concepts presented in the videos. The Tech-Cheks test video content and the Worksheets provide practical applications.

Practical . . . content-filled

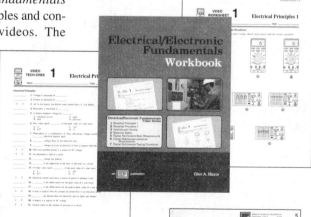

ELECTRICAL/ELECTRONIC SYMBOLS TRANSPARENCIES

By Glen A. Mazur

24 transparencies show symbols and abbreviations for common electrical/electronic components.

Transparencies   1770-4

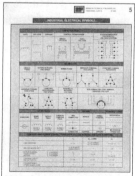

TROUBLESHOOTING ELECTRICAL/ ELECTRONIC SYSTEMS

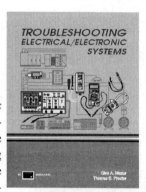

By Glen A. Mazur, Thomas E. Proctor

476 pages, heavily illustrated, soft cover.

Troubleshooting Electrical/Electronic Systems contains step-by-step Applications which show electrical and electronic troubleshooting methods. The Activities provide hands-on experience in solving troubleshooting problems. Topics covered include basic electrical theory, meters, motors, power distribution, lighting, programmable controllers, and preventive maintenance.

Text	1775-5
Instructor's Guide	1776-3
Workbook	1777-1
Instructor's Guide	1779-8
Transparencies	1777-1

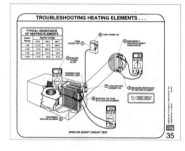

48 four-color transparencies

TROUBLESHOOTING ELECTRIC MOTORS

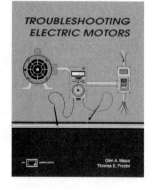

By Glen A. Mazur, Thomas E. Proctor

299 pages, 126 illustrations, soft cover.

This text/workbook covers operation and troubleshooting AC (single and three-phase), DC, and universal motors. Topics include motor characteristics, operation, loads, and mechanical conditions. Each chapter contains extensive review material and worksheets. The Instructor's Guide contains answers and solutions to the review materials and worksheets as well as tips for using the text.

Text	1762-3
Instructor's Guide	1763-1
Transparencies	1764-X

BUILDING TRADES PRINTREADING - PART 1 Residential Construction 2nd Edition

By Thomas E. Proctor

218 pages, 250 illustrations, soft cover.

Our best-selling printreading text/workbook presents the essential elements for reading residential construction prints. Extensive sketching, review, and test activities at the end of each chapter. Includes a complete appendix and glossary.

Over 1200 questions and problems

| Text | 0443-2 |
| Instructor's Guide | 0444-0 |

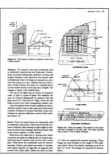

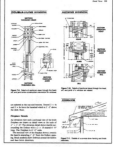

BUILDING TRADES PRINTREADING - PART 2 Residential and Light Commercial Construction 2nd Edition

By Thomas E. Proctor

370 pages, 178 illustrations, soft cover.

This heavily-illustrated and clearly written text contains plans for residential and light commercial construction. Topics include sketching, types of plans, specifications, abbreviations and symbols, specific building materials, and trade coordination.

| Text | 0421-1 |
| Instructor's Guide | 0422-X |

Over 1700 questions and problems

Ordering and Shipping

To order by mail or Fax:

- send your request to

  AMERICAN TECHNICAL PUBLISHERS, INC.
  1155 West 175th Street
  Homewood, Illinois 60430

- Fax **1-708-957-1137**

The following information is needed to fill your order:

- school or company name
- name and department
- street address
- city, state, and zip code
- area code and telephone number
- title, edition, book number, and quantity (ISBN prefix is 0-8269)
- authorization of payment (VISA, MasterCard, American Express, Purchase Order number, or check)

To order by telephone:

- call TOLL-FREE **1-800-323-3471** (7 AM–5 PM Central Time)
- have VISA, MasterCard, American Express, or Purchase Order number ready.

Shipping charges:

$00.00 to $30.00	$3.50
$30.01 to $40.00	$4.50
$40.01 to $50.00	$5.50
$50.01 and up	$6.50

Call 1-800-323-3471 for current prices.

Write a Book and Help Others Build the Skills that Build America!

At American Tech we're firmly committed to producing quality textbooks and related material that will help build the skills that build America. We welcome your ideas for new textbooks and encourage you to submit a proposal for a textbook.

If you would like, we'll send you a complimentary copy of *Author's Guide*, which explains how to turn your ideas into a book.

To order or for additional information, call today
TOLL-FREE **1-800-323-3471** or Fax **1-708-957-1137**.
We accept VISA, MasterCard, and American Express.